THE FUTURE REINVENTED

Reimagining Life, Society, and Business

D0302223

www.fastfuture.com

THE FUTURE REINVENTED

First published in United Kingdom and United States of America by

Fast Future Publishing in 2017

http://www.fastfuture.com

For Information contact info@fastfuture.com

Copyright © Fast Future Publishing Ltd 2017

Paperback ISBN 978-0-9932958-9-8

eBook ISBN 978-0-9932958-8-1

Cover Designed by Dusan Arsenic

Interior design and typesetting by April Koury

Print production in the UK by Print Trail

THE FUTURE REINVENTED

Reimagining Life, Society, and Business

Authors

Rohit Talwar
Steve Wells
Alexandra Whittington
April Koury
Maria Romero

Edited by

Rohit Talwar

www.fastfuture.com

About Fast Future

Fast Future is a professional foresight firm specializing in delivering keynote speeches, executive education, research, and consulting on the emerging future and the impacts of change for global clients. We publish books from leading future thinkers around the world, exploring how developments such as AI, robotics, exponential technologies, and disruptive thinking could impact individuals, societies, businesses, and governments and create the trillion-dollar sectors of the future. Fast Future has a particular focus on ensuring these advances are harnessed to unleash individual potential and enable a very human future.

www.fastfuture.com
Twitter @fastfuture @futrbiz
www.facebook.com/FutrBiz/
www.linkedin.com/company/fast-future-publishing/

The Authors

Rohit Talwar is a global futurist, award-winning keynote speaker, author, and the CEO of Fast Future. His prime focus is on helping clients understand and shape the emerging future by putting people at the center of the agenda. Rohit is the co-author of *Designing Your Future*, lead editor and a contributing author for *The Future of Business* and *Beyond Genuine Stupidity – Ensuring AI Serves Humanity*, editor of *Technology vs. Humanity*, and co-editor and contributor for two forthcoming books: *Unleashing Human Potential – The Future of AI in Business*, and *50:50 – Scenarios for the Next 50 Years*.

rohit@fastfuture.com
Twitter @fastfuture
www.facebook.com/RohitKTalwar
www.linkedin.com/in/talwar

Steve Wells is an experienced strategist, keynote speaker, futures analyst, partnership working practitioner, and the COO of Fast Future. He has a particular interest in helping clients anticipate and respond to the disruptive bursts of technological possibility that are shaping the emerging future. Steve is a contributor to *Beyond Genuine Stupidity – Ensuring AI Serves Humanity* and a co-editor of *The Future of Business, Technology vs. Humanity*, and forthcoming books on *Unleashing Human Potential – The Future of AI in Business* and *50:50 – Scenarios for the Next 50 Years*.

steve@fastfuture.com
Twitter @informingchoice
www.facebook.com/stevewells.futurist
www.linkedin.com/in/wellssteve/

Alexandra Whittington is a futurist, writer, foresight director of Fast Future, and faculty member on the Futures program at the University of Houston. She has a particular expertise in future visioning and scenario planning. Alexandra is a contributor to *The Future of Business* and *Beyond Genuine Stupidity – Ensuring AI Serves Humanity*, and a co-editor for forthcoming books on *Unleashing Human Potential – The Future of AI in Business* and *50:50 – Scenarios for the Next 50 Years*.

alex@fastfuture.com
Twitter @alexandra4casts
www.linkedin.com/in/alexandra-whittington-86794876

April Koury is a foresight researcher, writer, and the publishing director of Fast Future. She has worked on a range of foresight initiatives including society and media in 2020, emerging economies, and the future of travel, tourism, and transportation. April is a co-editor of *The Future of Business, Technology vs. Humanity,* and *Beyond Genuine Stupidity – Ensuring AI Serves Humanity* and two forthcoming books on *Unleashing Human Potential – The Future of AI in Business* and *50:50 – Scenarios for the Next 50 Years*.

april@fastfuture.com
www.linkedin.com/in/april-koury-20b04396/

Maria Romero was a futurist and foresight researcher at Fast Future. She has worked on a range of foresight initiatives including a project for NASA's Langley Research Center and the publication of "The Future of Student Life: Living" in *On The Horizon*. Maria is a contributor to *Unleashing Human Potential – The Future of AI in Business* and co-editor of *Beyond Genuine Stupidity – Ensuring AI Serves Humanity*.

www.linkedin.com/in/mgromerom/

Contents

REIMAGINING BUSINESS

CONCLUSION – CRITICAL SHIFTS DRIVING THE REINVENTION

Introduction

By Rohit Talwar and Maria Romero

The Future Reinvented – Reimagining Life, Society, and Business

The Future Reinvented – Reimagining Life, Society, and Business is an invitation to explore alternative—and sometimes competing—perspectives on how our collective futures may play out. The challenge for all of us is to try and form plausible but sufficiently stretching views of how the next decade could unfold under the influence of an ever-growing array of often exponentially accelerating forces of change.

Humanity today really does sit in the eye of a fast-moving storm that is combining and reinforcing major drivers of change from across the spectrum. These encompass politics, macro-economics, business and commerce, society, demographics, science, technology, energy, the environment, laws and regulations, moral choices, and our ethical frameworks.

When we take a step back to examine this constantly evolving and emerging landscape, it becomes clear that most of us have been, and perhaps still are, basing our planning assumptions on an expected future that is unlikely to materialize. On the contrary, these forces are breaking with tradition and expectation and are developing in unpredictable ways and at a pace few of us can keep up with. In short, we are witnessing a total transformation of the expected future, encompassing every aspect of life on our planet. This is the story we are exploring in *The Future Reinvented – Reimagining Life, Society, and Business*.

This second book in the **Fast Future** series, explores the major trends, forces, developments, and ideas shaping the next future. Our aim is to highlight how society's received wisdom, assumptions, and collective notions of the future are themselves undergoing a process of reinvention. Our goal is to encourage readers to challenge both "the official view" and your own perspectives on which changes will have the most impact. Our intention is to help you reimagine how life, society, key industries, and the conduct of business could be transformed in the decade ahead.

The Past is Not a Roadmap or a Destination

Often when organizations and individuals try to envision their future, they base their visions and strategies on solving past and current challenges. They try to project current trends into the future, and naturally assume or hope that progress will happen at a relatively steady, evolutionary pace. Technology inevitably plays a starring role in any such future narrative, even if we are a little sketchy on the implementation detail.

Interestingly, those that do have a sense of how deeply exponential technologies could impact our world can be somewhat overawed by the scale of potential changes and the societal implications. Those who seek answers or reassurance tend to be left unsatisfied with the responses to their concerns; indeed, in the name of progress, governments, the technology community, and techno-progressive thinkers often swat aside questions over whether the technology can actually deliver the goods, how society might react, and how we ensure fair and open access to such life-governing advances. In fact, they use past industrial revolutions and technological disruptions as evidence that human ingenuity has always left humanity better off.

The core arguments of the techno-optimists are that firstly the concerns being raised over issues like technological unemployment don't take account of the opportunities that will be created in sectors and businesses that don't yet exist. Secondly, they suggest that these technologies will deliver abundance and hence eliminate the need for us to work in dangerous or tedious jobs. They envisage a miraculous shift in public consciousness, where being unemployed is seen as a way of being that allows us to pursue our true purpose and express ourselves as oil painters, poets, and landscape gardeners.

Clearly, exponential technologies will undoubtedly play a fundamental part of our daily lives. In some quarters, there is almost breathless excitement at the increasing blurring of boundaries between the realms of science fantasy or magic and the technological realities that are unfolding. In every aspect of life, society, and business there are a seemingly endless array of opportunities emerging today or on the not too distant horizon.

However, perhaps our biggest challenge and opportunity is ensuring humanity survives and thrives in this technological utopia. We cannot place blind faith in technology to solve our biggest global challenges. Nor can we assume that artificial intelligence (AI) will always make choices that maximize the benefit to the largest number of people. We are at point in history where a wake-up call is resonating across the planet. In this book, we aim to highlight how we can heed that call and harness the immense power of science and technology to help us reimagine life, society, and business in a manner that ensures a very human future for all.

Embracing the Fourth Industrial Revolution

Historically, each economic revolution has been characterized by the introduction of science and technology breakthroughs that accelerated the production and distribution of goods and services. The First Industrial Revolution between 1760 and 1840 gave birth to the iron and textile industries and saw the use of water and the steam engine to mechanize production and power new factories across Europe and America. The transition from agrarian to industrial economy saw a reduction of physical labor demand in rural areas. Job opportunities shifted to the cities, and people followed the money to ensure their survival.

The Second Industrial Revolution took place between 1870 and 1914, and heralded advances such as electricity, the light bulb, and the telephone, which in turn enabled rapid industrialization and globalization. Established industrial sectors were disrupted, new ones emerged, and key infrastructure services were expanded rapidly, including rail networks, and public gas, water, and sewage systems. Production lines, nightshifts, and lower transportation costs changed social dynamics within families, communities, and workplaces.

The Third Industrial Revolution, or "Digital Revolution," started around 1969 with the rise of nuclear power, a shift to microelectronics from analog and mechanical devices, and the resulting development of sectors such as space exploration and biotechnology. Globalization contributed to this next wave of change—and was accelerated by it—pushing people together and accelerating the development of cities.

The convergence of information and communication technologies (ICT) and the rise of the Internet are perhaps the main symbols of the global impact of this revolution. The transformation from analog to digital revealed that software is cheaper and more efficient than salaried employees, which in turn pushed workers from manufacturing to the service industries. Unfortunately, better technology has not necessarily guaranteed enough or better jobs for all.

According to the World Economic Forum, we are entering an era of smart technologies, and a Fourth Industrial Revolution is emerging which will see us incorporate these advances into societies and humans themselves.[1] Following Moore's law, technology that was available a decade ago is becoming better. Most fields of ICT are progressing at least exponentially, enabling more functions, and are easily accessible through a plethora of applications and devices.

We've entered an era where general-purpose technologies like computers, tablets, and smartphones can perform a myriad of tasks just by changing the software. This set of mainly mobile hardware platforms provides the foundation for the waves of digital transformation now sweeping the planet and encompassing every aspect of human activity.

The exponentially progressing science and technology developments shaping the Fourth Industrial Revolution include: augmented reality (AR), artificial intelligence, autonomous vehicles, big data, biomimicry, blockchain, cloud computing, DNA computing, drones, genetics, human brain and body enhancements, hyperconnectivity, the Internet of things (IoT), nanotechnology, smart materials, organic and synthetic chemistry, quantum computing, renewable energy, robotics, sensors, synthetic biology, virtual reality (VR), and 3D/4D printing.

The key here is that the seeds of the next future are already planted and growing fast. Whether applied individually or in combination with each other, this array of innovations could dramatically impact life, society, and business in the near future. Across the globe, people are developing, researching, regulating, and consuming the early stages of these advancements. The choices these individuals make every day serve to nudge the future in a certain direction—but they are not all heading the same way, which makes the uncertainty of the outcomes even more interesting.

Decision making is largely based on historic data, in the form of experience or knowledge, which anticipates an outcome. Social values and cultural practices also influence this process by providing general moral guidelines. However, the future will not necessarily resemble the past and these technologies are already altering our moral compasses. Individuals' behavior, relationships, and expectations are shifting because of technology, but this cause-and-effect relationship is reciprocal. So, how can we help others prepare for the impacts the Fourth Industrial Revolution might have on their lives, society, and businesses?

Exploring the Next Future

The Future Reinvented – Reimagining Life, Society, and Business is designed to help expand our current decision-making process by considering alternative visions of the future and challenging our biases, as individuals and organizations. Each chapter explores a different aspect of the possible future and raises questions to help us think about the ways in which the developments being discussed could have an impact for individuals, societies, businesses, and governments.

Whilst we have included some more playful and exploratory predictions, the majority of the chapters focus on exploring a range of possible scenarios and conditional "what if" questions. These are powerful tools for exploring different possible outcomes when a range of forces come together. As futurists, we are trained to ask our clients and ourselves these questions on a constant basis. The reasoning behind this is that the future is not a defined destination, but on the contrary, a set of chaotic paths where the slightest change in the starting conditions or direction of travel could influence the end outcome quite dramatically. Thus, instead of trying to predict and plan for the prime or preferred scenario, the futurist approach is to try and create a comprehensive and resilient strategy that takes into consideration a range of different possible futures.

However, in order to reinvent the future, we need to unveil and understand what our current driving assumptions and default images are of how the next decade may play out. Only by assessing where we are starting from can we begin to think about different possibilities to the "almost probable certain future" we had been planning for and how to get somewhere else. This part of the process is about challenging our own biases.

Although our preconceived notions may seem harmless or unrelated to planning for the future, they may be blocking our ability to grasp opportunities or challenges on the horizon. We may be clinging on to ideas about how the world and our markets operate that are no longer a valid or helpful abstraction, or a good working simplification, of how things work. In fact, they may be taking us down a potentially dangerous alley that could lead to bad life choices or the failure of our organization.

Opening up to new ideas, different perspectives, and totally different ways of thinking about the future in general, and in our sector in particular, is critical to the process of conceiving alternative possible futures. We can explore diverse perspectives on the future by talking to those already embracing a different worldview, and metaphorically stepping into the shoes of competitors and new entrants who are pursuing wildly divergent strategies to ourselves. We can also tap into different futures perspectives both by consulting players across our value chain and by working with diverse teams within the business to help develop insight into, and empathy for, their views on how the world is changing.

The last part of reinventing our path to future is understanding how time sensitive the actions are. A small variation in the pace of change could lead to a very different set of futures: Being second or third to market with a new proposition might help us save on market development costs, but would still allow us to take advantage of scarcity, novelty, and premium pricing opportunities; being among the last to enter may mean we are already competing in a low margin, commoditized space before we've gained any learning to drive efficiencies in the cost of our go-to market offerings and delivery processes.

In a complex world where wicked problems are comprised of many different, interconnected, and fast changing parts, timing is everything. A small delay can lead to yet another related issue coming onto our radar, or more competitors entering the market and redefining expectations around the characteristics and pricing of the offering. Hence, this book highlights examples of ideas, issues, forces, trends, and developments that we should be discussing and acting on in the near future before they shift from being enticing opportunities, to challenges, or crises.

Reframing Life

Reimagining life implies forming new creative and resourceful ideas, images, and concepts of how we might live in the future; conceiving how we might harness technology innovations to service humanity's best interests. As mentioned above, in the past, the introduction of revolutionary technologies has impacted humanity at different levels. Moving to the city, using electricity, teleworking, and sharing across the Internet have all been life changing events enabled by technological advances. Now these activities have become part of normal life.

So, how quickly would we take it for granted if our next vehicle could drive itself or fly? Where would you go? How would you use it? How would that change where you live or the relationship you have with your family? Moreover, would you buy it, lease it, or just subscribe to its services? How would this influence the way you perceive its primary purpose, your definition of a car, and what you do in it? Similar types of questions apply to every technology that could impact our world. For example, what if our smartphone in 2020 could run our daily lives and conduct conversations on our behalf?

Imagine this avalanche of questions and uncertainties that will arise when it's not only your automobile that is smarter. What happens when there is intelligence built into the appliances in your home, the software at work, the gadgets and toys used by kids to learn and play, and the daily transactions and interactions you make? When combined, the technologies leading the Fourth Industrial Revolution could have an exponentially transformational effect on our lives. Hence, rather than responding after it happens, we need to be proactive.

We hope that by helping you, the reader, to think creatively about the different possible pathways and developments ahead, this will support and inspire you to create an image of one or more futures that you aspire to live in. An authentic personal vision can serve as a valuable tool in your decision- making—testing each option against it to see if a particular choice would take you towards or away from your preferred future. That vision might look totally different from today; the key is investing the time to understand the developments and choices that could help you take each successive step towards your desired outcome—remembering that the journey itself is normally more valuable and developmental than the destination, and that the vision may evolve as new possibilities unfold.

Rethinking Society

A key theme explored in the book is how society and our organizing structures and norms might be impacted by, and adapt to, the potential changes on the horizon. For more than two centuries, societies have largely organized themselves around the notions of work and learning how to work. The societal goal for almost every human is that we become productive individuals according to predetermined and accepted standards of expected contribution, largely based on our location, social class, and education level. In return, the payoff for the individual is that he or she can earn enough to live, feed, shelter, and clothe their dependents and, maybe one day, reach economic independence.

However, the intrinsic values, ideas, and assumptions upon which these foundational social structures depend are about to get disturbed. We simply don't know and can't yet predict the impact of these exponential technologies on jobs and employment. However, it is fair to assume that there will be significant upheaval—whether most human jobs are automated or there is a dramatic growth of employment opportunities in the industries of tomorrow such as autonomous cars and human augmentation.

Hence, we have to consider the scenarios that differ most from our current assumptions and ask how would we organize society if there were no jobs to do or schools to attend? What would people do if they no longer have to work for a living? What if the foundational societal concepts of careers, leisure time, and retirement disappear? What if these primary aspects of existence vanish amid the Fourth Industrial Revolution?

This transition could be exponentially rapid, confusing, and excruciating, especially if we ignore all the signposts of impending change and fail to act preemptively. Clearly, it is difficult to imagine how societal dynamics and our collective behavior might be disrupted. However, governments can run pilot exercises to explore different possible policy options and their second and third order societal impacts. For example, to counter the risks of mass unemployment, countries such as Canada, Finland, Namibia, and India are experimenting with programs offering a guaranteed or universal basic income (UBI). Already, they are providing valuable insights on implementing different approaches, possible benefits, and unexpected outcomes.

The Future Reinvented – Reimagining Life, Society, and Business sets out to provide examples of how our lives and the functioning of society could be transformed, facilitated by emerging science and technologies. The topics explored range from the near-term trends that could have a longer term impact, to the future of cities, the UK post-Brexit, retirement, education, and the potential to enhance our brains and bodies.

Reimagining Industries and the Future of Business

Perhaps the most obvious impacts of all the changes being discussed in this book will be on the structure and behavior of key industries, and on the purpose, strategy, and organization of business. Nowadays, businesses are the backbone of every contemporary society, which means they sit at the heart of each successive wave of transformational change. As we have witnessed before, enterprises can become vulnerable in unstable times if they are not open to new thinking, experimenting with new ideas, and evolving as quickly as the world around them. Those organizations that fail to ride each wave of innovation runs the risk of drowning due to a lack of a forward-looking culture and mindset.

The new, ever-smarter, and ever-more powerful technologies coming into the workplace can tempt us into choices driven by a desire to maximize cost efficiency and productivity, and thus replacing as many human employees as possible. While this strategy may seem like the obvious solution to today's problems, it might well be the wrong choice for tomorrow.

The risk of automating too far and commoditizing your product or service is very real, as is that of losing the trust of loyal customers because we have so few people left to serve them. The key to survival in the digital age will almost certainly be our ability to use the technology to help unleash human talent. For some time to come, people will still be our best resource to solve wicked problems, serve non-standard customer requests, develop new offerings, and identify new market opportunities.

There is a growing understanding of the major threat total automation represents to the viability of any kind of business. Hence, forward-thinking companies are also investing time and resources to experiment with different organizational forms including cooperative business models and concepts like crowdsourcing and open source platforms. These firms are testing their own physical and mental boundaries and their ability to redefine themselves and what they are capable of.

Many organizations are starting to see that the future is becoming less about assets and balance sheets and more about capability and connection. In the emerging landscape, our true value will increasingly lie in the capacity to implement good ideas quickly, learn from each iteration, refine and repeat. Crucial to such an experimentation-led approach is the nurturing of internal talent.

Models of tomorrow's business are predicated on the engagement of a constantly evolving network, or ecosystem, of external people and agents—partners who the firm supports, encourages, and inspires to help open up and service new markets and opportunities. However, in the constantly evolving model of the networked enterprise, there are also new responsibilities and standards to follow and create. Developing and maintaining real and transparent relationships with all stakeholders will become ever-more important, harder to do, but increasingly profitable and personally enriching.

The Future Reinvented – Reimagining Life, Society, and Business highlights examples of how a range of industry sectors could redefine their role and purpose, harnessing an array of new technologies to deliver fundamentally different product and service propositions. The final section on reimagining business explores how we can place people and ethics at the heart of the agenda, harness emerging technologies to drive growth and transform key business functions.

Chapter Introductions

The Future Reinvented – Reimagining Life, Society, and Business is a collection of the Fast Future's team most recent thinking on upcoming developments and their potential implications for humanity. The book features a total of twenty-three chapters organized into three sections, each focusing on a different level of transformation: life and society, industry, and business. To help you select the topics you most want to read about, we have summarized the content of each chapter below.

Reimagining Life and Society

1. *The Next Future – 40 Key Trends Shaping the Emerging Landscape* – An overview of forty critical drivers of change across societies that might emerge in 2018, and the possible extent of their impacts over the next five years. Topics encompass lifestyle, politics, people and the workplace, transport, and technology.

2. *Dear Dad: A Letter from a Brighter Future* – A snapshot into an optimistic future where society, politics, environment, economics, and technology interact harmoniously.

3. *Dear Mum: A Letter from Another Future* – A missive from a son to his mother about the struggles of a future filled with technology failing to fulfill its promise, severe economic inequality, ongoing social turmoil, and environmental hardship.

4. *The Future of Work: Retirement in a Post-Work Future* – An overview of the emerging roles for older workers in the Fourth Industrial Revolution, and the possible elimination of retirement.

5. *Intelligent, Connected, and Mobile – Scenarios for Smart, Sustainable, Human Cities* – Scenarios for three smart and very human metropolises of 2030, each highlighting a key driver: data management, artificial intelligence, and green energy.

6. *Britain 2022: The Future Beyond Brexit* – A summary of the results of a flash opinion poll on the future of the UK beyond Brexit, including priorities around social issues, science and technology, and the commercial world.

7. *The Gifts that Keep on Giving: 25 Human Transformations for Your 2030 Christmas Shopping List* – An overview of possible human augmentations, enhancements, and extensions that could become available over the next fifteen years.

8. *Digital Literacy in An Age of Exponential ICT Change* – Arguing the case for raising digital literacy so that we can ensure that information and communications technologies are harnessed to serve society.

Reimagining Industries

9. *The Emergence of Artificial Intelligence in Healthcare* – A synopsis of key areas where current and potential applications of AI might have an important impact in the healthcare.

10. *Won't Get Fooled Again: Anticipating Surprises in an Unpredictable Business Environment for Travel, Hospitality, and Business Events* – A review of eight key trends that could have growing relevance to the travel, hospitality, and business meeting sector.

11. *Authenticating the Travel Experience with Blockchain*– A reflection on potential applications of blockchain and cryptocurrency to reinforce trust and authenticity in the travel industry.

12. *Exploring the Future of Automotive in a World of Disruption* – An overview of transformational changes on the horizon for the automotive industry and smart highways sector.

13. *Follow the Money – The Future Evolution of Automotive Markets* – Highlighting five key drivers of change and their possible outcomes in a human-centered automotive industry.

14. *AI and the Legal Sector: Gift Bearing Friend or Havoc-Wreaking Foe?* – An examination of how law firms have the

opportunity to reinvent the industry from the insight out, from predicting case outcomes to developing new regulatory frameworks.

15. *Blockchain, Bitcoin, and Law: A Distributed Disruption?* – An analysis on applications and implications of blockchain and Bitcoin in the future of the legal industry.

16. *Educating the City of the Future: A Lifewide Learning Experience* – An exploration of the potential effects of smart city planning on education, including around the clock learning, civic engagement, and technology in the classroom.

17. *Food Production in a Hyper-Tech Future: Robochefs, VR Taste Tests, and Lab–Grown Meat?* – A peek into the technological developments that could emerge in food industry production, distribution, and retailing over the next ten years.

Reimagining Business

18. *Businesses and Technology – Time for a Code of Ethics?* – A discussion about the adoption of industry-wide moral standards around the uses of exponential technologies, plus recommendations on creating a digital ethics code for your organization.

19. *Staying Relevant – Five Fundamentals of Leading the Future for HR and Training* – Examining key actions forward-looking businesses need to take to cope with the upcoming challenges of technological disruption.

20. *A Tomorrow Fit for Humans – Ten Priorities for the HR Director* – A review of critical developments for HR directors and leaders to monitor and focus on over the coming years.

21. *Driving Online Sales Growth – Winning in the Wild World* – Four critical factors to focus on when developing a business plan for driving the future of online sales.

22. *Buliding Treasury's Digital Culture – Harnessing Next Generation Technologies* – Exploring the potential evolution of the corporate Treasury and the skills required to deliver it.

REIMAGINING LIFE AND SOCIETY

The Next Future – 40 Key Trends Shaping the Emerging Landscape

Dear Dad: A Letter from a Brighter Future

Dear Mum: A Letter from Another Future

The Future of Work: Retirement in a Post-Work Future

Intelligent, Connected, and Mobile – Scenarios for Smart, Sustainable, Human Cities

Britain 2022: The Future Beyond Brexit

The Gifts that Keep on Giving: 25 Human Transformations for Your 2030 Christmas Shopping List

Digital Literacy in an Age of Exponential ICT Change

The Next Future – 40 Key Trends Shaping the Emerging Landscape

By Rohit Talwar, Steve Wells, Alexandra Whittington, April Koury,
and Maria Romero

*What developments might emerge in the near-term future given
all the unruly technologists with their magical new toys, industry
upheavals, and complex social, economic, and political forces we can
see on the near horizon?*

In our recently launched book *Beyond Genuine Stupidity: Ensuring AI
Serves Humanity,* we highlighted a range of ways in which artificial
intelligence (AI) in particular could have a transformative impact for
individuals, society, business, and government in the coming years.
There are also a range of other exponentially improving technologies which could have a dramatic impact on society in the decade
ahead—including robotics, augmented (AR) and virtual reality (VR),
blockchain, 3D/4D printing, synthetic biology, and nanotechnology.

However, the future is about far more than technology, and so, in
these predictions, we have combined hard data on emerging trends
with some creative exploration on our part to explore the developments we might see emerging and playing out over the next five to
ten years. We cover both the use of disruptive technologies and the
broader societal and economic changes and developments that might

play out in the near-future. To help challenge the reader, the predictions also range from the highly plausible to wildcard developments that fall into the "unlikely but dramatic" category.

Society and Lifestyles

1. *Hollywood/Bollywood #metoo Slowdown* – The success of the #metoo campaign in surfacing female harassment will strike deep into major film studios and a broader range of sectors around the world during 2018. Whether through public exposure or private pressure from actors refusing to work with certain directors and producers, many of the accused will choose to resign or be forced to step down from their productions. This leads to regular production delays on a number of films and a noticeable slowdown in output and hence poor commercial results for many studios. The net result is that studios start to change their production model, with heavy vetting of those involved.

   Directors, producers and actors are forced to take out insurance policies indemnifying the studios against harassment lawsuits and the costs of any production delays. By 2023, we also see a big cultural shift in the studio system, with many more women in executive, production, and directorial roles. The rise of ethical and female-led independent film production further challenges the power of the big studios. The continuing rise of more accessible distribution channels and technology to develop film projects means that more independently produced movies are able to capture audiences.

2. *The Queen Abdicates* – In a move which shocks the media and the part of the nation that pays attention to such things, Her Majesty the Queen of the United Kingdom, Canada, Australia, and New Zealand announces that she is abdicating the throne in 2018 in favor of her son Prince Charles. The Queen indicates that she would like to slow down, spend more time with her husband Prince Philip, and act in an advisory capacity to the new King Charles. Written into the strict terms of the abdication

agreement is the condition that Charles himself must in turn abdicate by December 31st, 2023 in favor of his son Prince William.

3. *Facts as an Art Form: The Post-Truth Society* – Terms like "regulatory alignment," "alternative facts," and the "post truth society" have recently entered our vocabularies and will be much overused in the year ahead. The main concern is that it will require advanced AI to fact check everything before we can accept something is both true and has evidentiary support. At one level, these terms are amusing descriptions of a subculture where some believe that there is a very distant relationship between the "facts" and what is actually said or shared by those in power.

    The problem will be highlighted most acutely in the discussions around the UK's exit from the European Union. The true shape, costs, impacts, and benefits of Brexit will become the dominant talking point for many in politics and the media, and may not be fully clarified even a decade from now. At a deeper level, these issues highlight an erosion of trust in the veracity of what governments, businesses, public agencies, the media, and fellow citizens are saying. As individuals, we crave honesty and naturally favor organizations that we trust inherently. This offers a critical future opportunity for individuals, organizations, and governments to differentiate themselves because of their commitment to radical transparency.

4. *Robo-Dating* – Want your date to hang on your every word, never interrupt, and always do what you want? The first matchmaking websites will appear for those who want to date physical robots or virtual avatars—with personalities customized to our precise preferences. Around the world, women's groups will rise up in protest at services that they perceive as objectifying and dehumanizing women and returning them to the role of fawning 1950s housewives. Within five years, the systems will be using AI to determine and create our perfect match and allow us to have real babies with our robo-partners using donors and surrogates.

5. *Robo-Pop* – 2018 will see the first pop song written by AI enter the top 20 of the pop charts in a major economy such

as South Korea or Japan. By 2023, predictive algorithms will be used to determine the music and lyrics for over 50% of number ones, with the majority written by AI software.

6. *NFL/Premier League Player Strike* – Concerns over the treatment of black people by the police spurs a global movement with sports stars taking the lead. This culminates in a weekend of strikes in October 2018 with black players participating from the US National Football League (NFL), the English Premier, many other football leagues across Europe, and sports like cricket, baseball, and basketball. While progress on the underlying cause is slow, this becomes an annual event, and by 2023 has almost become a date in the sporting calendar.

Technology Transforming Life

7. *Artificial Intelligence vs. Genuine Stupidity* – Artificial intelligence is no longer the stuff of science fiction. From airline autopilots to smartphones and call center chatbots to automated legal contract generation, the technology is firmly embedded in society. The year ahead will see its scope, functionality, and processing power increasing. Sadly, many will continue to refuse to invest the time to understand how AI could transform their lives.

   For those in positions of power in business and government, there will still be reluctance to examining how AI could create new threats and generate new opportunities. Under the guise of pragmatism and risk avoidance, they will actually be putting the future of their business at risk. Others will recognize that carving out a small amount of time to understand the technology, how it is being applied, and what it could mean for their sector will help them deepen their understanding and form a perspective on how and when to approach it.

8. *Human Augmentation* – The trend towards people enhancing their brains and bodies is only likely to accelerate. The year ahead will see a mix of excitement and outcry at the proliferation of examples of people receiving chemical, genetic,

physical, and electronic augmentations of their "version 1.0" human brains and bodies. Over the next five years, it will be increasingly commonplace for people to use nootropic drugs and supplements to enhance their cognitive capacity.

Dramatic progress will also be made in the use of genetic modification techniques to change everything from eye color and hair thickness to skin pigmentation. Similarly, the use of external exoskeletons and internal endoskeletons, 3D printed body parts, and super smart materials would also enable physical augmentations that could make us stronger, faster, and less susceptible to pain. The age of the superhuman is beginning, and governments and businesses alike need to think about the pros of cons of encouraging such practices and addressing their potential impact across organizations and society as a whole.

9. *Robo-Store* – Around the world, 2018 sees a spate of openings of fully automated robo-stores where customers either wave and pay, or they are identified through facial recognition and their account is debited automatically. Robots serve customers, re-stock shelves, and self-organize to change displays rapidly based on their analysis of recent visitor and buyer behaviors. Home delivery can also be arranged using drones and pavement delivery robots. The automation of retail accelerates over the next few years and, by 2023, entire shopping malls promote themselves as fully automated. Human store staff are basically there to act as personal shoppers and customer advisers— powered by deep insight provided by the in store AI systems.

10. *Head/Body Transplants* – Following their much-disputed claims of completing a successful human head transplant to a corpse in 2017, controversial surgeon Professor Sergio Canavero and his team repeat the experiment in front of international observers in 2018. The individual survives less than 48 hours, but the observers acknowledge that the experiment was successful. By the end of 2023, the technique has been refined and there are now more than ten people around the world who are still alive six months after their transplant operation.

11. *Cryo Queen* – Hot on the heels of the announcement of her planned abdication by year end, 2018 sees the Queen also announce that she will have her body cryogenically preserved on death. The hope is that the technology to rejuvenate her body and restore her memory and consciousness will have emerged within 20 to 50 years. The intention is twofold: firstly, to give future generations access to the wisdom and experience the Queen has amassed over more than nine decades; secondly, to give a major boost to the UK cryogenics industry as one of the new sectors that will carry the UK economy forward post-Brexit. Within five years, the entire UK royal family, most senior UK political figures have all committed themselves to cryogenics. They are then followed by several prominent business people, performing artists, sports stars, and media personalities—with many becoming shareholders in the leading cryo service providers.

12. *AI Newscaster* – During 2018 a robot equipped with AI is used by a major news channel in the Middle East to work alongside a human, reading out the daily news and interviewing guests. As media budgets come under pressure in the increasingly automated world of 2023, the robo-casters have become commonplace in broadcast news services and online channels. We may pay a premium for a personalized newscaster who sounds like Meryl Streep, Stephen Hawking, or Beyoncé. For the majority receiving the public services from the news channels, our AI has been fed thousands of hours of news reporting in order to learn to flawlessly mimic the serious and situationally appropriate tone of the channels' best human newscasters.

Politics

13. *Polibots/Roboticians* – The first robot will be fielded as a political candidate somewhere in the world in 2018, probably by a fringe party. By 2023 South Korea, Iceland, and several others will have updated their constitutions to give robots equal rights to humans in parliament. In the next few years, the first robot MP will take their seat in a national

parliament, consulting and polling their electorate electronically on every issue in real time via the internet before casting its vote and displaying a 100% attendance record.

14. *Trump and Kim Play Cards* – Brinkmanship is dialed down dramatically in the second half of 2018. This comes after a massive build-up of US military presence along both of North Korea's coastlines and direct threats from President Trump to annihilate North Korea. In a bizarre turn of events, a meeting is brokered between President Trump and President Kim Jong-un in Japan with former basketball star Dennis Rodman acting as the go-between. Kim Jong-un insists that the leaders play poker to "break the ice," believing Trump to be beatable. While the result is never officially released by the US, North Korean TV claims it as the first of many victories in the meeting. Progress in thawing relations between the two nations remains slow, but in 2023 the US does send food aid via South Korea to help the North deal with a devastating drought.

15. *Country Mergers* – The perilous state of Zimbabwe's economy becomes more apparent post-Mugabe. The nation's leaders turn to South Africa for support in late 2018 and Zimbabwe effectively becomes a protectorate. Almost all arms of government come under South Africa control or supervision by 2023 and, to all effects, Zimbabwe is now its tenth province. A similar pattern is repeated around the world with more than 20 bankrupt or failing countries adopting similar protectorate arrangements under the instruction and supervision of the International Monetary Fund, World Bank, and United Nations.

The Economy

16. *Brokenomics/Economic Warfare: Stuck in the Middle* – There is a growing awareness that the economic, financial, and monetary control systems that govern our world have become overly complex and unworkable. The year ahead will see a growing number of governments, global institutions, business leaders, and civil society organizations publicly acknowledging this

and emphasizing the need for change. Many of these systems were designed for a previous pre-internet era and have been extended long beyond their useful life. They now represent a source of significant risk for the global economy. Emerging risks include an estimated US$1 quadrillion plus in derivative contracts against a global GDP that is valued at about US$75 trillion. Alongside this are seemingly non-viable pension systems, and personal, corporate, and government debt obligations collectively running at many times global GDP.

In the face of these potential economic time bombs, our financial and monetary governance mechanisms no longer seem fit for purpose. At the same time, more nationalistic political agendas are arising around the world and could drive intense economic warfare. Experimentation with new models will take place over the next few years, albeit at a very slow pace. A major new financial meltdown could accelerate that process.

Firms are already finding themselves stuck in the middle between shareholders and regulators and will increasingly come under government pressure to invest locally rather than internationally. Robust scenario planning and a rapid execution capability are both vital in these circumstances. The former can help explore the possibilities and map out the options; the latter can help reduce the time to value and avoid projects being lost in limbo.

17. *Pound – Dollar Parity* – The continued strength of the US economy, a favorable US stock market response to President Trump's tax plans, and chaotic uncertainty around Brexit all serve to drive down the value of the pound to parity with the US dollar during 2018. Following erratic gyrations which take the pound below US$1 during the Brexit wilderness years of 2019-2021, the UK economy eventually reaches a level of calm by 2022 as the shape of the new semi-Brexit clarifies. The pound settles at an exchange rate of around US$1.10 by 2023.

18. *Zero Growth Nation* – UK growth will plummet to zero and below in 2018. Brexit concerns will see more companies

leave the UK, while those that stay will reign in spending and engage in deep discounting. Households will cut their spending amid concerns over personal debt and job prospects as public-sector redundancies rise; more jobs are lost to automation; and firms cut headcounts to reduce costs. Other major nations also see growth stalling, but few hit the buffers like the UK. After a chaotic few years of Brexit mayhem, growth starts to stabilize by 2022 and crawls above 1% in 2023.

19. *Bitcoin at US$50,000* – Speculation will drive the price of Bitcoin to at least US$50,000 during 2018. This will further drive down the levels of Bitcoin's commercial use for transaction purposes, as coin holders will hang on to them as an appreciating asset. Within the next two years, China will announce its own government backed digital currency. This will see rapid adoption by several countries that will also outlaw Bitcoin and its rivals.

    By 2023, the price of Bitcoin, like many other competitors, will decline sharply as it returns to its role as just another digital currency, predominantly used for trading purposes. Massive losses are incurred by individuals, investment funds, and even countries who invested heavily in Bitcoin on the way up, but didn't sell out their positions quickly enough before the crash.

20. *The Artificial Economist* – Around the world, AI programs will outperform economists, analysts, and stock pickers in predicting what will happen to major stock markets, exchange rates, GDP figures, and bank base rates across the major economies by the end of 2018. Over the next few years, the number of new AI-powered FinTech funds at first proliferates and then plateaus and declines, with a number outperforming the market and some delivering unprecedented returns to investors. A wave of consolidations, mergers, and closures follows.

    By 2023, AI is either running or central to the management of more than half of the major public investment funds, unit trusts, investment trusts, and the like in the largest economies. Around the world, we also see AI being given a seat on investment bank boards, central bank advisory boards, and government monetary policy committees.

Transport

21. *Driverless Everywhere* – All around the world in 2018, we will see pilot schemes to test fully autonomous electric vehicles on the road, operating under normal driving conditions. China will be the first to actually have driverless cars driving alongside human-operated vehicles on a regular basis. The growing Chinese middle class flocks to purchase their first autonomous vehicle because these cars become a new status symbol. As a result, vehicle pollution in cities like Beijing will start to decline, slowly at first and then demonstrably.

    Motivated in part by the targets in the Paris climate agreement, more than 25 countries will have fully functional driverless green energy vehicles available for sale or hire by 2023. By then we could also see the first city authority introduce restrictions on manually driven cars in favor of autonomous vehicles.

22. *Flying Taxis* – following successful trials of single person passenger drones in 2017, commercial services are launched in China and the UAE during 2018. The technology continues to improve over the next few years, despite some fatal accidents and many near misses. Around the world, by 2023 more than 20 countries have licensed the use of both single and multiple occupant passenger drones.

23. *Supersonic Travel* – In 2018, we will see the first test flights of a supersonic flight from one of the new entrants such as Boom or Cygnus. When fully operational, these planes will be able to cover a range of up to 7,000 miles at speeds of 1,400 miles per hour, and are planned to be in commercial service by 2023.

24. *Hyperloop* – During 2018 at least 10 countries will follow the lead of the UAE and India, and sign up to have superfast (600-1,200 kilometers per hour) Hyperloop rail services in their countries within five years. Near full speed prototypes

are likely to be demonstrated during the year, and commercial Hyperloop services should be present in Asia, the Middle East, Europe, and possibly California by 2023.

Strategic Management of Business

25. *Cognitive Dissonance: Long Term vs. Right Here and Now* – The year ahead will see many leaders continue to be challenged with how to deal with a growing leadership juggling act. On the one hand, they can see quite clearly that radical changes are taking place and a very different future is emerging. However, on the ground, this isn't always reflected in the immediate requests coming from customers. They also know from experience that change starts off imperceptibly slowly at first, and then the take-off can often happen very fast.

   The tension between focusing on the here and now and allocating time and resource to an uncertain future is likely to grow rapidly. Developing the capacity to lead in this new normal will become a differentiator between winners and losers. Hence, a critical priority will be learning how to balance the "urgency of the now" with the "importance of the next."

26. *Future Awareness* – Businesses typically fall into three categories when it comes to future readiness: Firstly, some organizations and their leaders can rightly be proud of their level of awareness about the drivers of change that might shape their world in the coming years, and they are prepared for a range of possible scenarios. They typically have strategies that can kick in if the economy nosedives or if growth opportunities develop faster than initially expected.

   The second group is often oblivious to change or deliberately ignore it. They seem happy to rest on their laurels, believing they are bulletproof, that their offerings are always going to be in demand, and that their client relationships are cast in stone. This group is often the slowest to respond to change and tend to feel the most negative impacts when it happens, as they are least prepared for it.

The third and final group is honest enough to say they are uncertain about what might happen next, how change might impact them, or how to prepare for future uncertainty.

Knowing where you stand is a critical start point. The next step is to ensure that across the organization, leaders and managers are investing their own time and encouraging their staff to scan the horizon, read about impending changes, and think about possible implications and responses. If they lead by example, their teams will follow.

27. *Starting from Zero* – In the past, companies might have started their annual planning knowing that at least some proportion of business income was repeatable and that they would see recurring revenues in the year ahead. However, in many cases, contracts are shortening, retainer relationships are being dissolved, and organizations are obliged to start from zero when analyzing next year's revenues sources.

Budgeting from zero is a mindset and capability that will be developed and adopted increasingly across a range of industries in the coming year. At one extreme, this will drive firms to reduce headcount and adopt a more contingent workforce model; at the other we will see innovative strategies to try and open up new markets and lock-in longer term customer commitments.

28. *Exponential Organizations* – The coming year will see businesses of all sizes and many governments focus their attention on the idea of driving exponential or bigger improvements at speed. Most commentators focus on the big technology-enabled examples, e.g. Airbnb handling 90 times more bedrooms per employee than the typical hotel group or Local Motors generating new car designs for its 3D printed Strati 1000 times cheaper than the average car manufacturer. However, equally attractive are the simple innovations that can deliver rapid improvements—such as airports introducing parallel loading bays at security checkpoints to double or triple the flow of passengers. Leaders will be expected to encourage the pursuit of exponential gains and lead by example in the search for opportunities.

29. *Ecosystem Thinking* – Faced with the complexity of modern business, rapidly changing markets, short-lived opportunities, and exponential rates of development in technology, firms will have little choice but to work with a network of external partners. The year ahead will see a lot more experimentation with the use of ecosystems to absorb the constant onslaught of change and provide the capacity to respond faster. The next five years will see a mindset shift taking place, moving from "not invented here" to "which provider can do it better, cheaper, and faster." To make these ecosystem models work, there will be a critical requirement to develop leaders, managers, and staff with a collaborative mentality and a willingness to share, learn, and create solutions in partnership rather than by diktat.

30. *Gagging on Green* – In the coming few years of greater global uncertainty, firms may find it an increasing challenge to honor their environmental targets in an unpredictable commercial landscape. Failure to do so could ruin their reputation. Over the coming years, many businesses will increasingly be adopting the policy of pushing the responsibility to suppliers—demanding that they meet both cost and environmental requirements in order to win supply contracts. Others may seek low or no-cost ideas from staff that can be implemented quickly with little capital outlay.

Digital Choices

31. *Hooked on Transformation and the Race to Obsolescence* – In 2018, we could well see a pause for thought amongst large firms who are investing hundreds of millions of dollars on digital transformation projects. Many will realize they are just playing catch-up and trying to win the battles of the past ten years. They will also start to see the risks inherent in following the "cut and paste" prescriptions of advisers who are also promoting similar strategies to their competitors.

   Businesses will become more mindful of the inherent risk at the core of their digital strategy—namely that the faster we automate, the easier it is for others to copy what we do. The recognition will also grow of how hard it is to sustain a point of digital differentiation for any length of time. The risk is that many are locked in a race to the bottom, commoditizing their offering and potentially sowing the seeds of their own demise. A vital role here for leaders will be to challenge those involved, and ask them to explain how the outcomes will help us stand out and enable us to be more innovative and responsive than competitors pursuing a similar path.

32. *Born Digital and Hollow* – An increasing number of new businesses will be adopting a very lean resourcing model, automating wherever possible from the outset in their pursuit of exponential growth and the much coveted billion-dollar "Unicorn" valuation. Indeed, we will see a proliferation of so called distributed autonomous organizations (DAOs), companies that exist only in software and have no employees. By 2023 such entities will be far more widespread across a range of activities, including those that take place in the physical world.

    We can anticipate entirely digital versions of fast food chains, domestic service providers, and travel booking services. Whilst humans may do the ultimate physical service delivery, the underlying booking platform will exist entirely in software—imagine an Uber or Airbnb with no staff at head office. Inside larger firms, the next few years will see a critical and continuous conversation on how to monitor these digital entities. A key area for exploration and experimentation will be how to ensure the preservation of human talent, as it is still more capable than technology in spotting and responding innovatively to emerging changes, risks, and opportunities.

33. *I Serve the System: No Human to Turn To* – One of the most soul withering phrases we hear today is, "I'm sorry, the system won't let me do that." As we automate more and place increasing authority in the hands of technology, leaders will become increasingly mindful of what this could do to brand identity and the public discourse about us in social channels.

Firms will be experimenting with different delivery models and making clear choices over the extent to which they will allow humans to exercise discretion in the service of the customer. This will extend to working through what our back-up plan is when the technology fails in a highly-automated business, and evaluating whether there are differentiation opportunities in having a more human face to the business.

34. *Surveillance Capitalism* – In the pressurized economic environment of the coming years, many individuals will be ever more willing to give away their personal data. In return for "free" services, we may allow firms to make greater use of the content of our social media, emails, and online searches. The firms that provide these "free" services will deepen their focus on extracting valuable data from our activity, which can be resold and used to target us more effectively.

Within five years, if left unchecked, the penetration into our daily lives and personal activities could become all-pervasive. Indeed, some researchers suggest that, by using predictive analytics and machine learning tools to analyze between 64 and 200 of the items we like on Facebook, a detailed profile can be developed of everything from our likely purchasing behavior, through to what we might watch, and our voting intentions.

This notion of "surveillance capitalism" is likely to increase in the coming years. As businesses, we need to decide the extent to which we'll try to extract commercial value from our customer data, and whether we'll look to protect ourselves from others' exploiting the data we have provided.

People and the Workplace

35. *Swarm Organizations* – Persistent economic uncertainty will see a number of firms and governments cutting back to the barest minimum of human resources. Such organizations are increasingly likely to adopt an accelerated "swarm resourcing" concept to respond to new opportunities and urgent change projects.

This model is based on the approach favored by film producers—pulling together teams for critical projects on demand—drawing on contractors, partners, agencies, staff on zero-hour contracts, and internal resources. The core challenges here are getting the team formed, bonded, up to speed, aligned, and functional in the shortest possible time. This will see a lot of organizations putting the development and recruitment focus on having the right internal capability and management processes to support a swarm approach.

36. *Privacy vs. Performance in the Always-On Society* – In 2018, we will increasingly hear about firms that are able to monitor literally every employee all the time. This will be enabled by a range of workplace cameras, motion monitoring devices, sensors, and wearable technologies. The outputs from this "web of surveillance" will allow for a regime of total monitoring—especially when coupled with data from employees' mobile devices, laptops, and desktops.

    Firms will increasingly monitor factors such as concentration, reading rates, eyeball movement, mouse clicks, and typing speeds to assess employee productivity and determine when we are in and out of our peak performance states. There are obvious benefits to be gained from constantly tracking the health, well-being, and productivity of employees. Managers, employees, and governments will increasingly wrestle with whether this constitutes an infringement of rights or an invasion of privacy. A growing number might determine that the impacts on employee motivation and corporate reputation when adopting such "big brother" surveillance tactics might not be worth the risk.

37. *Alpha Male vs. Embracing the Feminine* – Across the board, 2018 will see firms responding to uncertainty by automating, becoming more number-focused, and adopting increasingly control-orientated thinking and management structures. There is a concern that these developments could drive out essential feminine traits that can

differentiate us in the marketplace—leading to a far more masculine business environment with a few short years.

The broader issue of gender imbalance will undoubtedly persist for some time to come as firms continue to fail to take full advantage of available talent. In addition, a rising concern would be the loss of feminine traits that help define our culture and distinguish our brand in the marketplace. Leaders will need to pay serious attention to the challenge of ensuring that crucial feminine factors such as culture, connection, serendipity, empathy, and compassion don't get devalued or eliminated as we pursue efficiency and give greater agency to the machine.

38. *Always on the Way Out and Something on the Side* – Someone entering the workforce at the age of eighteen today could easily live to a hundred and do anywhere from twenty to forty jobs in that time—if they are still working at all in fifty years' time. The years ahead will also see growing volatility in the recruitment market, particularly for younger workers. Hence, 2018 will highlight how new employees have an eye to the next job and many will be pursuing side-businesses, hopefully in their spare time. While such entrepreneurialism will increasingly be encouraged, firms will also be challenged to find ways of motivating and getting the full commitment of people who are "always on the way out" from the day they arrive.

39. *Workplace Stress* – The mental health challenges for society will rise to the top of the public discourse agenda in 2018. This will be driven by growing pressures on mental health, coupled with new concerns over the possible impacts of technological unemployment. Each successive wave of workplace research suggests that stress levels are rising and leading to unhealthy, unproductive, and potentially dysfunctional home and workplace behaviors.

The year ahead will see growing emphasis on mindfulness meditation, yoga, sleep advice, dietary improvements, and regular health checks to help mitigate stress. Alongside this we will see a growing exploration of more radical shifts in the way we run our businesses, set personal targets, measure performance, and manage people. Those firms which have the courage to pursue a different approach and offer an alternative, less damaging path to success will find themselves in greater demand as employers.

40. *A Very Human Business* – As a direct response to many of the forces outlined above, the next five years will see an exponentially growing number of businesses deliberately swimming against the tide and genuinely putting people at the heart of their strategies. While they will still be using technology, it will be seen as a productivity aid. The goal will be to help free up the time of smart people to engage more deeply with customers, develop new strategies, be creative, experiment, and build more sustainable points of difference that are embedded in people not technology.

- *What critical challenges might leaders in society, business, and government face as they take on the responsibility of shaping a very human future enabled by technology?*
- *How could individuals seize the benefits and opportunities arising from the potential disruptions shaping the decade ahead?*
- *What are the critical implications of these potentially radical shifts for the relationship between business leaders and their local communities?*

A version of this article was originally published in *Bytestart* under the title "The Future of Business – 20 Key Trends Leaders Should Know."

Dear Dad: A Letter from a Brighter Future

By Rohit Talwar and Katharine Barnett

How might emerging generations embrace an optimistic technology-enabled future?

Millennials and the generations that follow them are facing and shaping a radically different future from their parents' world. Powerful digital technologies are poised to bring seismic changes in lifestyles, opportunities, privileges, and choices experienced by young people compared to their ancestors. This letter from the future draws on some of those key developments to give dads a glimpse of what's over the horizon and what they should prepare themselves and their children for.

Dear Dad,

As I send you this message from December 31st 2030, here are some things I want you to anticipate and tell me about while I'm still young enough to list to you! In short, the world has transformed because of exponentially improving digital technologies that are coming together to change every aspect of our lives.

Everything and everyone is hyper-connected; all the big internet systems that dominate our lives talk to each other and combine our data—social behavior, viewing preferences, purchasing information, and other activities—so we get tailored content, news, and products. I've saved a huge amount of time because I started to watch only the shows that match my interests and preferences. The data gathered about us and our movements is used in so many different ways to help enhance every aspect of our lives—although you might think that intrusive. For example, our whereabouts data is also processed by artificial intelligence (AI) algorithms to help predict, pre-empt, and prevent crime. Moreover, when combined with data from traffic, construction areas, police, and planning departments, it can highlight possible danger zones and suggest ways to make them safer.

While all this surveillance has raised privacy concerns, the benefits more than compensate for the risks. I never worry where the kids are or if they are safe. I can see where they've been, track their location, and predict where they might be going on my holographic display mobile device. The new connectivity era has made constant interaction normal; the boundaries between private and public have been blurred—we are always in touch with others in some way.

I have an intelligent digital assistant (IDA); it lives in the cloud and accumulates all my data. It carries out everyday tasks, from booking a restaurant to searching for a travel route, to even updating my doctor with my health status. Dad, I want you to know that there's been a revolution in healthcare. Now I don't need to concern myself with conditions like high cholesterol, hypertension, heart disease, and diabetes.

Personal health devices use nanotechnology, AI, and a wealth of web-based bio-tools to help manage our wellbeing. They don't just diagnose and treat illnesses, they also identify the underlying causes of conditions years before they appear and help prevent them. I have nano-devices medicine in my bloodstream, waiting to be activated to remove cancerous cells, perform tissue repair, or release drugs when needed. Again, I know you might think that this is invasive and doesn't give us healthcare choices, but Dad, you won't have to worry about remembering to take your medications—it's such a weight off our minds.

Almost everything has been automated—blue collar and white collar jobs have been taken over by machines. The traditional notion of working for a living has all but disappeared, and I have the option to work if I want to. This technological revolution has funded the provision of universal basic income (UBI) and universal basic services (UBS) for anyone that wants them. I never need to worry about paying the bills or the mortgage. There is so much freedom to pursue enjoyable activities, sports, and hobbies. I can watch the kids play football, drive to the countryside, or work on some DIY—without worrying about upcoming deadlines at work.

Burn out, anxiety, and stress are pretty much things of the past. Dad, you would really enjoy our lifestyles. This work revolution has changed our social system, too. Healthy life spans and UBI have negated the need for retirement plans—my family and I are going to live healthily into our nineties with a secure income. I don't have to worry about a retirement plan! It's wonderful to know that we can spend so much more time with our families and loved ones; I think I'm even going to get to see my great-great grandchildren.

Things in 2030 have transformed so dramatically, and all the things I can see and experience are so radically different from my childhood. Dad I know you think that these changes are extreme and revolutionary, but they are so wonderful that I must share them with you. The future is, quite literally, awesome.

With love,
Katharine

- *How might different societies and governments react to receiving this information about the future?*
- *How might such an optimistic image of the future encourage people to shape their aspirational choices?*
- *Which aspects of the future are most and least appealing to you personally, and which would most enhance your life?*

A version of this article was originally published in *Dad* under the titleA Letter from the Future: Dear Dad."

Dear Mum: A Letter from Another Future

By Rohit Talwar and Alexandra Whittington

What would be the consequences of a future where technology fails to deliver and the environmental crisis peaks?

In the previous chapter we presented an optimistic "Dear Dad" letter from the future highlighting how technological advances could enhance our lives over the next ten to fifteen years. To balance the blatant optimism of this first letter, and being true to our futurist calling, here we present alternative perspective of how things might play out: a letter from another future.

This letter is sent on Mother's Day 2030. While "Dear Dad" paints a daughter's picture of technological utopia and abundant opportunities, the "Dear Mum" future presented here shares a son's account of societal decline, highlighting what could happen if we collectively ignore the signals of impending change and some of our worst fears come true.

In this more dystopian future, water, food, and natural resources run short, thanks in part to basic supplies being horded by the wealthy. A huge rich-poor divide in incomes and wealth forms the basis for civic unrest. At the same time, innovation lies dormant, forming a technological vacuum—an expanded and more pervasive second artificial intelligence (AI) winter that spans a broader range of technologies.

This innovation trough catches the modern world by surprise, causing discomfort and contributing to many points of tension. A major category of social unrest that plagues this future is inter-generational conflict, with the young feeling betrayed by the choices of their elders. The dark future scenario "Dear Mum" contains fears, challenges, warnings, and regrets—four horsemen of the global governance apocalypse that a futurist perspective is meant to prepare us for and inoculate against.

Dear Mum,

It's been ten years since you passed and we last spoke, but you asked me to write to you today, a decade on— for Mother's Day—to tell you what has happened to the world you left behind. I think the massive loss of human life has caused the most pain across the planet, and was perhaps the biggest and most avoidable legacy of those who've run the world for the last 100 years. The pain caused by this global death toll is matched and possibly exceeded by a deep sense of regret.

There is a sense of "global knowing" that, while there was so much that could have been done, so little was actually achieved because of politics, egos, ambition, greed, and financially motivated governance choices. Even though I personally consider you innocent, there are many who condemn you and your entire generation for allowing the rot to set in "on your watch."

I agree that everyone born before 2000 is complicit in causing this chain of catastrophic suffering. But it actually accelerated since you died ten years ago. I find it hard to blame you for something that was the byproduct of decades of cultural escapism—and that only spiraled out of control after it had claimed you as a victim.

The first thing I want to ask is, why didn't anyone listen? For decades, scientists, philosophers, and experts across every domain from climate science and AI, to biodiversity and disease control had been warning us of the growing list of exponential risks. They warned, in ever more frantic terms, of the unseen and potentially irreversible threats arising from our pursuit of stellar profits through unregulated, unchecked, and largely uncontrolled exponential advances in science and technology. Indeed, you were still here in May 2017 when the scientist Stephen Hawking warned that humanity only had 100 years to get off planet earth. This was hardly the first such cataclysmic warning—in fact it was one of the last.

So, what actually happened? Well, pretty soon after you left us, things began to fall apart quite dramatically as far as ecological stability was concerned. Extreme weather and rising sea levels proved highly disruptive to a number of systems like agriculture, transportation, travel, and communications. Rising temperatures accelerated mass migration from hard hit regions and caused violent and chaotic scenes at many country borders. Indeed, rumors and video evidence abounded of government militias exterminating entire cohorts of refugees arriving at their borders and sinking overcrowded boats at sea.

Climate chaos also interfered with information and communication technology (ICT) systems, with networks collapsing and servers failing under the heat. This of course led to a number of problems with basically every aspect of life and the economy. Education, work, and public services became unstable and unreliable. In rapid succession supply chains broke down, raw material costs rose, the price of literally everything skyrocketed, and inflation naturally went off the charts.

The chaos meant that financial markets inevitably went into meltdown, banks collapsed, and governments were unable to underwrite the losses of those who saw their savings disappear. Companies slashed their workforces, wages fell, and few nations had any kind of workable schemes to provide guaranteed basic incomes and services. Countries around the world fell into recession leading to extreme social chaos and major economic losses.

There was so much despair from this combination of economic chaos, internet blackouts, and interruption of the electrical grid, and people grew more and more mistrustful and survival focused. Communities disintegrated—there were regular violent outbreaks in many of the worlds' biggest cities. The chaos reinforced the rich-poor divide and increased the already disproportionate power imbalances. Those with wealth found it even easier to secure control over the provision of basic goods and services, supported as they were by fear-driven policies that effectively repressed the poor and enriched the already well-off.

Governments caved in to the demands of the super-rich and ceded ever greater control of public assets to the rich elite in return for guarantees that they would stay in the country, pay at least some taxes, and spend money in the economy. Income inequality rose exponentially, which led to distrust in every corner of society. Priorities shifted from preserving the status quo, to very overtly protecting the interests of the few. This acted as a tipping point for social unrest given the already tenuous imbalances between socioeconomic classes. Rather than seek to bridge a growing gap, the world's decision makers chose to protect the few and sacrifice the many.

Ecological degradation led to widespread shortages of food and clean water. Natural systems were known to be vulnerable since the mid-2010s, and these issues led rapidly to an acceleration of observable and adverse natural phenomena. Various species displayed random and aberrant patterns, such as bee die-offs, loss of entire sub-species and varieties, amphibian mutations, and plant flowerings that defied seasons. These environmental shifts had a sudden impact on the food supply, a scenario dozens of scientists had seen coming.

Hunger became a global norm again, and while governments worked at a rather pedestrian pace and in a very tokenistic way to try to solve the problem, there was very little that could be done. For example, it was difficult to accelerate promising food science initiatives or overcome years of lax environmental policies, particularly in the developed world. Water and sanitation suffered as well, and clean sources became few and far between. Believe it or not, water access in 2030 is rationed, unpredictable, and conflict-ridden.

Mum, if somehow you are reading this, you must be thinking, "She's got this all wrong." When you were still alive, we knew these problems were coming up, but we also thought that technology-enabled innovation and human ingenuity would save us. We thought renewable energy would replace the dirty fracking and fossil fuel mining, which had contaminated so much land and water. We thought 3D printed food, laboratory grown meat, and genetically modified organisms would help feed the entire planet safely and cheaply. We hoped that personal technology and a world powered by AI would offer a pathway to more equal, transparent, and politically empowered societies.

We often talked about how the solutions just needed to be invented and that they were right around the corner. What we didn't realize or accept was that a technological fix is just not enough. We are now learning that it takes very different mindsets, coupled with serious attitudinal reframing, behavioral shifts, and cultural change to get us out of our self-inflicted mess. A big shock has been the failure of some of our most promising technologies, which has occurred since you passed away ten years ago.

Back then, we thought that by 2025 AI, blockchain, 3D printing, and an internet of smart things would enable our deliverance from tenuous living conditions. However, by 2022 the public backlash against these technologies was in full swing and governments tried to control their development using heavy-handed and retrograde measures rather than forward thinking approaches. This led to a sharp decline in funding for research and development and a dramatic slowdown progress—and they have not yet picked back up. Most expect they never will, at least not in our lifetimes, which means not in time to save human life on earth.

Technological innovation was also dampened by the depressed spirit of the times, Moore's law no longer applies, and we are seeing almost no improvements in computing power rather than the exponential gains Moore had predicted. Indeed, the last ten years have been a sort of Dark Age in terms of progress in science and technology. The fact that educational systems are so crippled and outdated hasn't helped. Schools have closed or been merged, classroom sizes have tripled in some areas, and teachers' pay has been frozen for five years after a series of real-term cuts.

Academic research programs have been de-funded, and entire universities, colleges, faculties, and departments have closed in higher education. Those schools and degree programs that do survive rely on the sponsorship of rich local benefactors. These new funders are in turn guaranteed a percentage of the lifetime income of every student they support, collected for them by government via the tax system. I never did finish my degree, Mum. Last time I saw you I was beginning my second year at university, but I never got to finish because I had to focus on survival, as did most of my other friends and classmates.

I know you were a victim, too. Cancer has always been a common cause of death, but in your case the environmental source of the disease has a sad irony; there is now clear proof that the pesticides, used to treat the crops that once grew so bountifully, were also slowly killing us. Our ability to feed so many so well was such a noble idea but ultimately not in our best interests.

Society learned too late that large-scale agriculture put far too much pressure on natural systems and poisoned the water supply. The resulting food crisis has taught us to respect the systems that give us life, and use them in a more healthy way. Unfortunately it is too late for victims like you, innocent martyrs to global mismanagement. But in a way, I'm glad you're not here to see it yourself. I think you'd be saddened by all the ways in which humanity has sold itself short.

With love,
Alex

- *How might different societies and governments react to receiving this information about the future?*
- *How might such a pessimistic image of the future encourage people to change behavior and shape their choices?*
- *How should society balance its efforts and resources between building an aspirational future and also preparing for more pessimistic scenarios?*

The Future of Work: Retirement in a Post-Work Future

By Rohit Talwar, Alexandra Whittington, Steve Wells, April Koury, Karolina Dolatowska, and Maria Romero

What opportunities and challenges could arise for older workers in a post-jobs era?

Is the future for older workers bleak or blessed? So-called mainstream views of the future of work often strike highly pessimistic tones, perhaps with good reason. Some of the most-cited economic studies predict that half or more of all jobs could be taken over by machines within 20 to 30 years. The media can't help but remind us that with those jobs go people, paychecks, and possibly an entire way of life.

The silver lining to this news is that the rise of artificial intelligence (AI) should also create new jobs. Artificial intelligence is, ironically, a technology that could provide unique opportunities in attractive new work roles, and may actually have the particular impact of allowing people to work longer and more flexibly across life stages in the future.

A Human Touch: Emotional Intelligence
While the current climate around AI is thriving with breakthrough developments (like algorithms that can develop new recipes, create new baby names, or design clothes), there are still many areas where

AI is weak. So, for example, it is possible that one of the future roles for the over-50's would be in an AI training capacity, teaching algorithms how to do non-computational things that require a human touch. While training your own replacement sounds less than ideal, it may be highly rewarding to teach AIs to use empathy in dealing with customers. For instance, helping AIs relate to clients experiencing health difficulties, or to use the right language and tone when dealing with frustrated coworkers could both lead to very positive experiences for all concerned—and the AI will never tire or lose patience.

Any attribute of employee performance requiring emotional intelligence is currently difficult to program; instead, it could become an area where retired workers, the semi-retired, or "gig workers" with a portfolio of jobs, could tutor AI programs to learn. These roles would probably allow for a great deal of personal development and greater understanding of interpersonal relationships and would resemble more of a nurturing, teaching, almost parenting-like function. They could probably be flexible in terms of hours and projects, which might be something retirees would welcome.

Guardians of What Matters

Another plausible future worth consideration for adults close to retirement is one where the rise of AI in the coming decades leads to the risk of important sources of traditional knowledge being lost. It is conceivable that nuanced things like manners, handwriting, water-cooler small talk, and humor could be some of the uniquely human characteristics that may prove difficult for smart machines to simulate. Therefore, is it imaginable that older, more experienced people could be valued for their social skills, and put to work in unconventional ways? Personalized tutoring in delicate and human customs could be a great job in which to spend our golden years.

Some people might be paid to just hang around a business in case a human touch is necessary. Visit upscale jewelry stores, boutiques, and hotels and one can see such roles already in existence. They would be reminiscent of the traditional role of elders in society, where the more experienced adults would be looked up to for wisdom, knowledge, and guidance instead of being rendered obsolete. Indeed, as technology creates pockets of artificiality via AI, virtual reality (VR), augmented reality (AR), and other forms of simulated reality, it will be more important than ever to provide an authentic human context in the workplace.

Celebrating the value of the wisdom of elders is a lost tradition that might be particularly powerful for the Google generation, providing balance in a future dominated by algorithms and computation. Would humans retain their claim over important capabilities like interpreting body language and sensitivity to awkward situations? Assuming such insight remains difficult to impart via code, protecting various forms of social conventions would have a special function in the automated workplace. Older people would be able to transmit and teach knowledge to younger co-workers that would otherwise have been lost.

When Work Disappears, So Will Retirement

Obviously, it is preferable that new tools support human-centric workplaces rather than replace jobs and expertise; indeed, the desired future is often the one that's easiest to see most clearly. In terms of AI, there's a tremendous promise of unleashing human potential, rather than limiting it. In doing so, it could revolutionize the traditional trajectory of working life, from foundational training to retirement. However, the ideal outcome, where AI complements rather than usurps humanity, depends on its implementation. Unlike previous technological revolutions like electricity and computerization that changed work, AI represents direct competition to human employees.

Companies are salivating at the chance to cut costs and obtain the efficiency, reliability, and consistency possible with AI. However, the societal-level changes that automation will entail, such as redefining work, or education, or even our life purpose, renders a profit-driven mindset insufficient. Rather, companies should look at AI as a way to foster life-long relationships with employees; for example, could we see employers providing AI assistants at work that go on to become home-care bots in our retirement years? Authentic displays of human decency in engaging with people at any career stage might be how organizations can build AI-enabled workforces of real value.

- *How might exponential technologies improve intergenerational relationships in the workplace?*
- *How could companies engage and retain experienced workers in a post-work future?*
- *How might technology best be deployed in businesses that emphasize providing a human touch in the care of retirees?*

A version of this article was originally published in *Silver Magazine* under the title "The future of work – retirement in an AI landscape."

Intelligent, Connected, and Mobile – Scenarios for Smart, Sustainable, Human Cities

By Rohit Talwar, Steve Wells, Alexandra Whittington, April Koury, and Maria Romero

How might technological advances in data management, artificial intelligence, and energy help shape the future of cities?

A vision of the "city of the future" is often presented as a compelling symbol of the direction in which society could progress. Whilst visions differ, the common element is the notion that in the future, Earth's most concentrated populations will occupy city environments where a digital blanket of sensors, devices, and cloud-connected data are brought together to enhance the living experience for all. Smart concepts encompass a range of key elements of what enable effective city ecosystems—from traffic control and environmental protection, to management of energy, sanitation, healthcare, security, and buildings.

Scenarios are a helpful tool to envision how human city visions might take shape over the next 10 to 15 years. Here we explore three 2030 scenarios showing how data, artificial intelligence (AI), and clean energy might deliver interconnected and seamless mobility in healthy, clean, smart, and livable cities.

Data

In 2030, Transport for London (TfL) runs Greater London's multimodal transport network using a fully integrated AI-based Travel and Transport Management System (TTMS). Vast amounts of data are processed using human expertise, AI-based transport infrastructure planning and traffic management algorithms, and predictive analysis—drawing on sensors in roads, pavements, and public transport access points. These are supplemented by video interpretation from 60,000 closed circuit TV (CCTV) cameras, which re-established London as the world's most watched city, surpassing Beijing. Traffic and pedestrian flows have grown exponentially, transport's environmental impacts have declined dramatically, and globally in 2030, London is ranked first on mobility.

A single control center automatically manages and matches services to demand—combining autonomous buses, surface and subway trains, and road and rail signaling. Live predictive analytics allow greater use of road and track space. Autonomous boats ply their trade on the Thames from Putney in the west to Woolwich Royal Arsenal in the east. An automated fail-safe mode restricts public access to capacity-sensitive areas like underground stations and riverboat piers.

Manual drive cars of all fuel types are still visible but only autonomous electrically powered vehicles are permitted in the city center Congestion Charge Area—a toll fee is automatically charged against the vehicle's account information held in a blockchain-based payment system. In the late 2010s, traffic controllers still manually changed timings at three quarters of London's traffic signals to reduce queues; now, the process is automated. A constant flow of data between autonomous vehicles (their current location, destination, purpose of the journey) and the central system is used to re-route traffic around congested areas. The system also gives priority to public transport and emergency services. The system's associated app also provides navigational information to pedestrians' personal digital assistants.

Embedded road sensors monitor surface and sub-surface conditions. Traffic types and flows are constantly tracked against the

TTMS' comprehensive historic road status database, which drives a program of proactive maintenance. This reduces requirements for lengthier and more extensive subsequent repairs. It also minimizes traffic disruption by accurately re-routing transport resources during repairs, maintenance, and emergency situations, and predicts the implications of any such situations.

For the first time since the horse and cart, London is (for the most part) moving freely again thanks to its fully integrated TTMS. Not only is London moving, but other major cities around the world are seeking London's expertise, creating unexpected revenues for TfL.

Artificial Intelligence

It's New Year's Eve 2029 and several hundred thousand people gather in Times Square to see in 2030. The all-encompassing role of smart, autonomous, self-managing vehicles is in full evidence across the city. As of tomorrow, only autonomous vehicles will be allowed on the streets except in a few designated zones and "drivers' parks" where enthusiasts will be able to take the controls.

Vehicle ownership is almost obsolete as most new vehicles are effectively self-owning. These independent taxis earn a fare for each ride and share revenues with those who manufacture, service, and refuel them. The cars work in self-managing, self-insuring networks, covering each other in the event of increasingly rare incidents. Autonomous technology grows ever smarter and accidents only tend to arise when human-driven vehicles are in collision with autonomous cars.

Revelers at the NYE celebrations can rest assured that a smartcab or personal drone will reach them within five minutes. Autonomous ambulances patrol the city with in-vehicle robots providing immediate first aid and carrying out more complex tasks under the guidance of remote doctors observing via video. Personal drones are used to extract the injured parties from their location and transport them to the ambulance. Autonomous food trucks serve revelers in public areas with drones delivering the food to the individual wherever they stand without having to navigate through the crowd. Single user "Dronejohns" or "Droneloos" can also be summoned on demand—dropping into the midst of the crowd to enable those caught short to relieve themselves in privacy.

Autonomous vehicles have changed city life, cutting congestion, reducing pollution, providing services on demand, and freeing up car parking for new uses and pop-up activities.

Energy

Martina and her friends have a meeting at the library after school. Even in 2030, homework is still an everyday occurrence here in Paris. Taking a driverless car from school to the library—a standard transportation option for schoolchildren—the girls walk in through the grand entranceway of the library. The historic library building is retrofitted with the smart technologies of 2030 without sacrificing the charm of the 1970's façade. Old buildings are precious in the city— the cost to upgrade them is offset by the carbon neutrality of new transportation solutions. The building is old, net zero, and smart: When someone is dropped off at the entrance, it lets the autonomous cars know which library patrons are ready to leave, or sends the car to another passenger nearby.

As the girls complete their work, they are earning social credits that will provide more free rides in the future; doing homework and other good deeds are a currency children use to get around town. Mobility had become a service as basic as electricity and internet access—and completely clean, safe, and renewable. Electric transportation options are around every corner in the form of public mass transport (self-driving buses and trains), drone taxis, and self-driving electric cars.

The scaling of apps and technology to intuitively offer "Mobility as a Service" (MaaS) across the city mean private cars and driving have become obsolete. Smart technologies are so advanced that users rarely need to request rides; they are predictively hailed by internet-connected things such as their watch, phone, home, or desk.

From the library, the autonomous car drives the girls to their various homes, lessons, or practices. The parents' digital assistants communicate with the city's main brain to agree different drop off locations for their children, ensuring no wasted trips. The smart city offers a lot for families: Parents are no longer caught in gridlock on long commutes to the suburbs since efficient city planning allows large numbers of residents to live in urban places comfortably and abundantly.

Planning for the Future of Cities

The smart city movement has the potential to transform the organization of people and physical objects in a way that transcends urban development as we know it. The shift to smart infrastructure is not simply fashionable or aspirational; in many ways, it appears to be a critical enabler of the future sustainability of cities. It can be argued that the future of human life on the planet rests on a smooth transition to cities that are more efficient, less wasteful, and more conscious of the impacts of the individual upon the greater good.

To achieve this vision, society must harness the impressive and increasing potential of the collective data drawn from large groups of people living together in cities. Who owns the data? Who decides how it is to be used? Where does the greater good overshadow individual free will, and vice versa? These are some questions that city planners and residents will need to build more dialogue around in order to ensure that future cities are intentionally wise and human, and not just smart.

- *How might social and family dynamics change as a result of these technological advances in the city?*
- *How might government, businesses, and society address the emerging issues of data privacy and security?*
- *How can we ensure genuine citizen engagement in envisioning smart cities and realizing the full benefits when they are in operation?*

A version of this article was originally published in *TransportXtra* under the title "Let's build smart, sustainable, human cities."

Britain 2022:
The Future Beyond Brexit

By Rohit Talwar, April Koury, and Alexandra Whittington

How can government and society build a collective aspirational future for the UK beyond Brexit?

The Future of Britain in 2022 – Electoral Priorities

This future priorities survey was conducted in the run up to the UK general election held on Thursday, June 8th, 2017. The results highlight deep doubts over Brexit, and emphasize citizen concerns over electoral reform, government investment in science and technology, renewable energy, health service effectiveness, retaining EU single market access, and modernizing the education system. We include the results in this book because we believe these long-term priorities should remain at the heart of government priorities as we determine the direction of the nation post-Brexit.

The Future of Britain 2022 – Survey Overview

The survey was conducted when campaigning for the UK election was in full swing, and Brexit appeared to be the dominant issue for the parties and the media. However, we wanted to look ahead to determine the longer-term issues citizens want politicians to be debating as we contemplate the next five years in a rapidly changing world. So, explore this question, Fast Future ran a flash survey from May 24th to

May 30th, 2017. The survey was distributed to our own networks and via a range of social media forums covering all points on the political spectrum. A total of 209 responses were received, with just over 78% of those who stated an origin coming from the UK.

Participants were asked a series of six multiple-choice questions covering Politics and Security, Social Issues, Economic Priorities, the Commercial World, Science and Technology Policy, and Environmental Priorities. For each question they were asked to select two options from a list of possibilities. For each question, they could also add their own thoughts and comments on alternative priorities. In a seventh open ended question, respondents were asked to suggest any other priorities that they considered critical to Britain's long-term future.

Presented on the following pages are the responses of both the total respondent base and also for those who selected the UK as their geographic origin. The accompanying narrative focuses mainly on the views of UK respondents, contrasting these, where relevant, with total responses and with the views of UK participants aged under 35.

Key Findings

Politics and Security – Electoral reform is the single biggest priority across all six questions, with 79% demanding discussion of a more representative electoral model. There is little support for discussing the underlying themes and ideas around Brexit such as adopting a "Britain first" stance in Brexit negotiations (9%), reducing immigration (7%), and strengthening Britain's relationship with the USA (0%).

Social Issues – Respondents want politicians to be focused on a more effective health service (47%), an education system that prepares pupils for a fast-changing world (40%), and establishing a more caring and compassionate society (32%).

Economic Priorities – Participants want a combination of continuity and solutions for impending disruption—hence among the UK responses, ensuring Britain retains access to the European single market (42%) was emphasized, along with redistribution of wealth to the poorest in society (36%), and preparing for the economic and social impact of the potential replacement of jobs with technology (29%). The under 35s displayed far more concern over future disruption and prioritized guaranteed basic incomes and services (58%), preparing for the impact of technology on jobs (42%), and wealth redistribution (42%).

Commercial World – A changing industrial mix and the rise of new sectors led to a clear focus on the need to develop human capital and encourage the creation of new ventures that can fill the potential employment gaps that might arise from technological disruption. The ideas prioritized included encouraging companies to spend more on training and development (34%), supporting the development of small to medium enterprises (33%), and creating incentives for businesses to generate jobs in their local communities (24%).

Science and Technology Policy – National capacity building to help the UK compete globally is clearly seen as a priority with an emphasis on increasing government investment in key fields of science and technology (55%), and raising technology awareness and digital literacy across society (30%).

Environmental Priorities – UK respondents are clear that renewable energy and a clean environment are key to ensuring a sustainable future for Britain, prioritizing accelerating investment in renewable energy generation (53%), increasing environmental protection (33%), improving air quality (19%), and stronger environmental legislation for businesses (19%).

Conclusions

The survey highlights the views of respondents across the political spectrum. There is an evident message that, despite concerns over Brexit, UK respondents want to look beyond the next two years of the Brexit process to focus on a progressive reform agenda designed to position the UK to be a major player on the global stage over the next five years. The scale of interest in electoral reform may come as the biggest surprise, but is an unequivocal reflection of the desire for more representative governance models. There is a clear sense that the global economy is being disrupted by exponentially advancing technologies such as artificial intelligence. UK respondents want to see government responding to help build the nation's capacity to innovate and the ability of individuals to survive and thrive in a fast changing world.

- *How could exponential technologies contribute to achieve the priorities highlighted by respondents?*
- *How could the UK government and society ensure a collaborative and mutually beneficial relationship with the EU?*
- *What changes might be required in the UK's social, economic, and political systems to ensure it remains a healthy, economically vibrant player on the global stage?*

A version of this article was originally published under the title "The Future of Britain 2022: Survey." Download and view the entire survey at fastfuture.com.

The Gifts that Keep on Giving: 25 Human Transformations for Your 2030 Christmas Shopping List

By Rohit Talwar, Steve Wells, Alexandra Whittington, April Koury, and Maria Romero

How might the most popular human augmentations impact our daily life over the next twenty years?

As we look to a world in which enhancement of the human brain and body are likely to become commonplace, a key question arises: Is a person still human if they are also enhanced, enriched, or augmented by technology? To help readers make their own decisions on this, here, in the spirit of the season, we offer a list of twenty-five human transformations that might make it onto the "must have" holiday shopping list of 2030. Which would you or your loved ones want?

First, most of the emerging transformational technologies aimed at human enhancement fall under a few general categories, despite a good deal of crossover. Here's a quick guide:

Chemical enhancement: Chemical enhancements would include pharmaceuticals which alter the brain, encompassing nootropics for focus and memory, or psychedelics for vision quests. Any transformation resulting from ingesting a food or drug would fall into this group.

Genetic enhancement: Targeting our DNA and genetics, this category of augmentations involves editing or altering the actual chromosomes and genomes before or after conception. The most commonly discussed technology for genetic enhancement today is CRISPR, a "cheap and easy" means of editing DNA in existing life forms. Genetic transformation also takes us into the realms cloning, designer babies, chimeras, and aging/disease prevention.

Neurological enhancement: Enhancements to the brain can take several forms ranging from hardware to software. Neural implants, electronic stimulation, and brain hacking all fall under this category—implants being actual foreign objects embedded in some way to affect the nervous system. Hacking could involve tapping into the brain via "mind over matter" or altered consciousness state to awaken previously dormant mental, physical, or even metaphysical abilities.

Physical enhancement: Physical transformations would usually appear as hardware add-ons like exoskeletons (i.e. an "Iron Man" suit), endoskeletons with reinforced bones, chip implantations, bionic eyes, or other prosthetics. These could be bionic, cyborg, 3D/4D printed, or otherwise innovative adaptations, which can either be removed (like prosthetics, clothing, or armor) or permanent (surgically attached or implanted). Genetic manipulation to achieve extreme physical beauty or strength would be included in this category.

Electronic enhancement: The use of electronics involves the transformation of intelligence, consciousness, or humanity into digital form. Any type of uploading or downloading of human "content" in digital data form (hard drives or to the cloud) could be considered an electronic enhancement. There may also be types of implants or tattoos that read vital signs to communicate them to the Internet of things (IoT), blockchains, or digital public health data sets. Health applications of nanotechnology could fall under this category along with wearable technology, and human transformations that deal with virtual reality (VR) or augmented reality (AR).

Radical life extension: Extending life often refers to "curing death" as its raison d'être. Aging is viewed as an unnecessary evil, a mere medical problem waiting to be solved. Being able to live 125 years or more with comfort and good health seems to be the current vision for life extension proponents, who advocate for pharmaceutical, dietary, and lifestyle adaptations to achieve longer than natural life spans.

Cryogenic freezing/Cryopreservation: Rather than extend life, this transformative breakthrough puts life on pause, to restart later in time, decades or centuries from now. The idea behind cryogenic freezing is that in the future, medical technology will be able to reanimate a body which has been preserved in liquid nitrogen at very low temperatures. The elderly and the terminally ill are the most likely candidates for cryo, although in the future there could also be elective preservation conducted for personal reasons by otherwise healthy people. Of course, we have no idea whether we'll ever have the technology to re-awaken the physical body and restore memory and consciousness.

The holiday shopping list of 2030 may contain several of these future transformations wrapped up in a neat package of human enhancements. Below are twenty-five radical suggestions you might treat your friends, colleagues, and family members to in the coming decades. Happy holidays!

1. *Instant Content Upgrades* – Uploading a new language, a map, knowledge about a client or project, and key information prior to a romantic date or a business meeting could be available over the next 10 to 15 years through instant content updates to the human brain. This would be achieved either

through direct downloads to our web-connected brains or via plug-in memory devices for more confidential information.

2. *Brain-Computer Interface* – Wireless communication between our brains and an array of connected devices could become a reality. From computers and phones, to domestic appliances and in-car entertainment systems—we would be able to operate gadgets with our thoughts. These wearable or implanted sensors and transmission devices would allow us to communicate as we do with Siri and Alexa today, but without saying a word.

3. *Smart Contact Lenses* – Who needs screens when you have eyes that can be turned into visual interfaces? Every device could easily connect with your smart contact lenses and present the information you desire such as augmented reality overlays of a city as you sightsee. Your requests would be communicated using eye movement, gestures, words, or telepathic commands.

4. *Beyond the Rainbow* – Gene therapy has cured color blindness in monkeys; if clinical trials are allowed, color blind humans may be next. Eventually, science may expand our color vision to include all wavelengths of light, from gamma rays to ultraviolet and even radio waves. Humans might literally see the world in a whole new light.

5. *Beyond Sound* – As humans age, we naturally lose the ability to hear higher frequencies. In the future, we may be able to reverse this, or even enhance human hearing beyond the normal range via aural implants directly connected to our brains.

6. *Endoskeleton* – Become stronger and fitter from the inside out, but without most of the requirement for exercise and healthy eating. Physical and genetic enhancements applied to your bones and muscles would improve your Body Mass Index (BMI) and performance from the get-go. Reinforced bones would improve tone and strength with no extra work needed.

7. *Implanted Immunity Bubble* – Subcutaneous implants would detect pathogens in the immediate environment and provide antibodies to protect us from specific contagious diseases. This

would make most public health measures irrelevant as coughing, sneezing, and touching may no longer pose a risk. Hand washing could become a redundant activity and vaccines unnecessary, while a global antibiotic crisis could also be averted.

8. *Heightened Sensitivity* – Through deep brain stimulation, humans may eventually have total control over how much physical sensations affect them. We could turn a dial to increase touch sensitivity during intimate moments, or while playing a car chase computer game, but dial down our sensitivity in anticipation of a physical altercation.

9. *Reality Check Implant* – This personal detection system would allow us to control our experience of mixed reality, virtual reality, and augmented reality sensory stimulation environments. The system would block out photoshopped, virtual, augmented, digital, or holographic imagery, and other sensory inputs whenever the wearer wants to "keep it real."

10. *Wear Your Reputation on Your Sleeve* – One's online reputation may become a valuable form of currency in the future, and be considered in job-seeking or credit applications, for example. Tattoos or embedded objects could change, grow, morph, and otherwise shape-shift depending on one's fluctuating online reputation score. A score might be comprised of the number of social media contacts, shares, likes, or uploads.

11. *Cosmetic Gene Editing* – The gene modification technology known as CRISPR introduced in 2012 has already made it "cheap and easy" to edit genomes inside the body. The CRISPR system's ease of use means it could be adopted for almost any gene-editing requirement. So, while doctors could apply the technology as a targeted cancer treatment, we could also see the same approach used for cosmetic augmentation. For example, shopping malls could provide services to change clients' hair thickness, eye color, and skin pigmentation, making CRISPR treatments as common as other beauty and lifestyle options.

12. *Immersive Experiential Technologies* – Augmented, multi-sensory, and immersive mixed or virtual reality could create opportunities for new types of life experience. For example, feeling the bed linen, tasting the food, and smelling the bathroom fragrances of a hotel on the other side of the world would be part of choosing where to visit. You could possibly consume a range of experiences direct from your living room, in place of travelling: Immerse yourself in the sights, sounds, and smells of the Serengeti while you eat your takeaway pizza in Brooklyn.

13. *3D Cloner: See and Print* – This device would allow a product to be identified and 3D printed in real time and "on sight." Special optical lens implants would trigger the cloning of the item being viewed by the wearer, like taking a snapshot. Clothing, food, and even medical products like prosthetic arms or legs could be created instantaneously on the spot, "cloning" whatever item the user glances at, and transmitting the design to be produced on 3D printing machines.

14. *The God Pill* – Advances in pharmaceuticals and neuroscience could lead to a breakthrough drug designed to experience a higher state of consciousness which some might call "God." This might provide a feeling of one's place in the universe, a sense of oneness with nature, or help you visualize yourself face to face with an actual deity. These hallucinogenic experiences would fall somewhere on a spectrum between recreational and therapeutic, depending on the recipient's state of mind at the time. This could be perfect for coping with mid-life crises, dealing with the death of a loved one, anxiety disorders, accepting a terminal diagnosis, and recovering from addiction. Or, just try it for fun.

15. *3D Printed Wings* – We could fly as close to the sun as we like with customized 3D printed wings, which are perfectly designed to bring aerodynamic freedom and flight. These powerful, lightweight appendages could be attached surgically and removed by a visiting robo-surgeon or with an in-home DIY kit and training video (sold separately).

16. *Always a Good Hair Day* – A gene-altering pill that could change a hairstyle within fifteen minutes from straight to curly would save time and energy since styling is eliminated from the daily routine, and there would be no need to visit the hair salon. Furthermore, toxic beauty products could be eliminated from daily regimens with this enhancement. This would also be ideal for traveling to extremely humid or dry climates. This pill's popularity could surge in regions where climate change is already having an effect.

17. *Virtual Reality Empathy Machine: Walk a Mile in My Shoes** – Conflict resolution would be simplified with virtual reality empathy films, which allow friends, family members, teachers, students, bosses, workers, and even litigators in court to literally see the world through each other's eyes. Benefits would include greater interpersonal intimacy and understanding, elimination of sibling rivalries, and dealing swiftly with difficult people. *Requires pre-installation of a memory recording device.

18. *Sleep with the Fishes* – Using "mind over matter" psychological approaches, hacking of the human body might someday allow people to breathe underwater. The brain would convince the body it has certain fish-like abilities—specifically, greater lung capacity. Humans could then live in futuristic underwater cities, engaging in a little live action role play as Aquaman or a mermaid, or just enjoy swimming with the dolphins during island vacations without scuba gear. Such an enhancement could also enable humans to settle or just vacation on floating or underwater cities without fear of drowning.

19. *Cryopreservation Pal* – Cryogenic freezing is a medical technology that preserves a human body in liquid nitrogen at very low temperatures, hopefully for later reanimation at some point in the future. A cryopreservation chamber, which fits one human and one dog or large cat, could make the deep sleep a bit less frightening. It would be nice to know your best friend will be there when you wake up in twenty or a hundred years' time. Instant companionship might make the idea of being

reanimated in the far future a little less daunting for people who don't have spouses or family members being cryopreserved.

20. *Perfect Body in a Pill* – What if, at last, medical science achieves the ultimate win for sofa surfers, and creates a pill to give you the body of a god without putting in all the work or adopting any healthy habits? Ripped abs, ageless skin, perfect proportions— what more could someone want? For those who do want more, a second daily pill could generate an intoxicating body odor.

21. *Exoskeleton* – Achieving superhuman strength and endurance might be possible with an exoskeleton suit of external body armor that turns any average person into Iron Man. Physical labor would be a breeze with the addition of robotic arms, legs, and a back which never tire or run low on energy. Whilst this would be great for work or recreational sports, it puts house movers, construction workers, and even weight lifters at risk of being "replaced by cyborgs."

22. *Elephant Man or Woman* – Imagine never forgetting anything ever again. Elephants are believed to have the longest memory of any living creature. With the help of neural implants, now people can remember forever, too! These implants, possibly in the form of a "neural lace" lattice of tiny sensors under or just above the skull, could improve memory, and may ultimately also prevent Alzheimer's disease. This would make a perfect gift for the radical age-extender in your life, or elderly relatives who've not yet shown signs of dementia.

23. *Digital Happy Pill* – Dwellers of the world's high-tech smart cities could opt to take a pill that lets them have their lives monitored and managed remotely with 24/7 data capture and surveillance, day in and day out. Imagine having each and every behavior monitored, and, if necessary, modified, by the city's central nervous system based on a smart city artificial intelligence program. One of the ways to alleviate fears, paranoias, or other mental delusions concerning "privacy" might be to take this daily "digital happy pill", jointly

monitored by city planners and medical professionals to ensure smart city residents are the happiest citizens on earth! Smile, you're on camera (constantly, even in your own home)!

24. *4D Printed Skin* – 4D printed materials are essentially "shape shifting" in the sense that they can change their form and properties based on external stimuli. So, wetness prompts drying or absorption, heat promotes cooling, and so forth. In the future, a skinsuit, active skin covering, or surgical skin implant could give humans the ability to adapt to their environment seamlessly. Clothing may become unnecessary with this form-fitting, shape-shifting material, which could look like clothes, skin, or whatever the wearer selects. An essential adaptation in extreme climates, 4D printed skin is also ideal for the fashionista in your life.

25. *Organ Regeneration* – The ability to regenerate human organs could end the ravages of disease, aging, and even injury. By 2030, organ regeneration modification may be the signature transformation of life-extension adopters. Careful consideration should be taken with the giving of this gift (particularly with alcoholics and drug abusers), as it could actually enable irresponsible behavior.

- *What enhancement or superpower would you most like to have?*
- *Where do we draw the line between human and bionic? Human and cyborg?*
- *Which traits could or should never be replicated by technology? Where is the line between enhancement and eugenics?*
- *What kind of legal framework would we need to develop in order to address the concerns around human augmentation?*

A version of this article was originally published under the title "The gifts that keep on giving: 25 human transformations for your 2030 Christmas shopping list."

Digital Literacy in an Age of Exponential ICT Change

By Rohit Talwar and Alexandra Whittington

How can we raise technological literacy levels to deal with the exponential advances of the Fourth Industrial Revolution?

The exponentially accelerating pace of development across a range of fields of science and technology is driving home the importance of raising technological literacy across society and at all levels of education and experience. So, what's driving the sense of urgency here? While the internet is the familiar overarching narrative when we talk about the digital future, there is much more happening in the field of information and communications technology (ICT).

The innovations that we already know about, such as cloud computing, social media, and big data, are not slowing down; quite the opposite actually, and represent just the start of the story. They are being joined on the technological landscape by a number of other exponentially improving technologies and the concepts they enable. Hence, the expected future is that, pretty soon, artificial intelligence (AI), drones, autonomous vehicles, and smart cities will be commonplace.

Wearable technologies will become implantable, nano-scale, and internal. Meanwhile mankind may surpass both normal life spans and the various natural genetic limitations such as susceptibility to disease. As these innovations evolve, futurists are taking up the often unpopular task of asking whether society wants or needs these changes, how to make decisions about them, and how to prepare everyone for their impact.

Today's most cutting-edge innovations in ICT are either already progressing exponentially or prone to do so some time soon. The internet, for example, is morphing into the Internet of things (IoT). This is just one manifestation of the approaching wave of exponential scientific and technological change coming in the next few years. To help understand exponential progress, let's start by thinking about making the normal, linear ascent up a staircase. Now imagine the alternative of leaping exponentially from step 1 to step 2 to step 4 to step 8 to step 16 and upwards—eventually skipping entire floors. The sheer scale of the possible changes means that a solid framework for understanding the potential impacts of these breakthroughs is critical if we are to elevate our culture to a higher level of technological literacy.

Although the concept of "technological literacy" can be ambiguous, and in the face of exponential change, it almost feels inadequate. It is an idea that can be expressed using several different terms and encompasses many different aspects of society's relationship with technology. A report published in 2000 by the OECD called Basic Skills in Adult Education and Bridging the Digital Divide used the term technological literacy to mean, "the ability to utilise ICT effectively."[2]

The Colorado Department of Education defines technology literacy as, "the ability to responsibly use appropriate technology to: communicate; solve problems; access, manage, integrate, evaluate, design, and create information to improve learning in all subject areas and acquire lifelong knowledge and skills in the 21st century."[3]

The highly respected International Society for Technology in Education (ISTE) describes digital literacy as a key component of digital citizenship. In the ISTE framework, digital literacy falls under the education category—addressing, "how to learn in a digital society."[4] Each definition seems to stress the same idea that the skills alone are not enough to constitute effective use of technology; some kind of evaluation or reflection on the appropriate and preferable outcomes of its use is required.

Closer to the cutting-edge, there are now education and training programs that utilize augmented (AR) and virtual reality (VR) in a variety of contexts from teaching 11-year-olds about genetics through to surgical training for medical students. Other such examples include Georgia Tech University running a course with a covert AI teaching assistant, and Teachur, the education start-up trying to put higher education on the blockchain.

Technology in instructional settings is sometimes taken for granted, or viewed instantly as an advantage, but their societal-level impacts are often inadequately evaluated. This is a key area for reflection as we accelerate into our technological future: The act of using ICT subtly implies our consent for its resultant impacts, the scale of which could rise as these shifts accelerate exponentially.

Technological literacy, or some version of it, is rapidly replacing "literacy" as the base skill in society; in 2018, a person who doesn't use the internet is like someone in the Westenr world in 1918 being unable to read. Take, for example, the smart phone. Today the non-smart phone user is increasingly disadvantaged, marginalized, and possibly viewed suspiciously as antisocial, deviant, or some other type of nonconformist.

Smart phones are valuable for web searching, accessing online applications, texting, social media, email, and (less and less) for phone calls. Few would argue that they do not serve a critical function in day-to-day life. However, they also contain GPS location devices and store mountains of private data about the user, including photos, passwords, and credit card information.

Clearly, no one would argue that smartphones are truly secure or that the data on one's phone is safe from spying eyes. Yet, how is it that the smart phone has come to possess so much of our identity and life, and signify our place as a functional member of society, i.e. technologically literate in the sense that this is appropriate use of the technology? Now, take for example, a person in 2018 who uses a landline exclusively: Compared to the person who trusts smart phones, which individual is displaying the correct level of technological literacy and secure technology usage?

Perhaps because it is the most familiar, the importance of the internet can obscure other transformative technologies. Scan the pages of this book and it becomes clear that it is not just the digital realm that is changing what it means to be human. Several other parallel technological innovations taking shape right now are contributing to the transformation. Indeed, these reach all the way to life span extension and human enhancement via implantable or wearable devices. So, while ICT is the most obvious and constant reminder of the cascade of technological shifts taking place, it is just one field out of many different science-led domains that are heading down the exponential path.

A higher level of technological literacy would help society take a realistic view of disruptive technologies and allow a more critical appraisal of the claims made by techno-optimists and the likely benefits to society as a whole. Some claim that the risks are overblown and that we should be seeking to accelerate, not dampen, the pace of technological progress. Others argue that these seductive technologies are unfolding in an uncontrolled and uncontrollable manner that could threaten human existence. As with any form of progress, the argument center on a core question: "Just because we can, does it mean we should?"

- *How can we govern technological advancements to ensure they bring social progress and opportunities for all?*
- *How could we bridge the technological gap for vulnerable populations like elders and those who live in remote areas?*
- *How can we help society as a whole to understand the critical differences between linear and exponential technological and social changes?*

A version of this article was originally published in *CILIP* under the title "Digital Literacy in An Age of Exponential ICT Change."

REIMAGINING INDUSTRIES

The Emergence of Artificial Intelligence in Healthcare

By Rohit Talwar and Katharine Barnett

What transformational opportunities and challenges are emerging from the application of artificial intelligence in the healthcare ecosystem?

Artificial intelligence (AI) is increasing in scale, power, and applicability. The technology is transforming businesses in every sector, including healthcare. Drug development, condition diagnosis, disease prediction, and patient management are all being disrupted by AI. In this chapter, we highlight key examples on the changes we may see, explore current AI developments and applications within the healthcare setting, examine their benefits, and discuss potential concerns that could arise around the use of AI in healthcare.

While AI in the broadest sense may be some way off, i.e. the ability to replicate the entire functioning of a human brain, AI in a narrow sense is already embedded in many of the systems, devices, and digital services we use. For example, digital assistants such as Siri, Cortana, and Amazon Echo all use AI to recognize speech patterns and run a growing range of processes to answer queries, search for information, and learn our needs and behaviors. Within healthcare, the range of current and potential applications is growing, as outlined below.

Diagnosis and Prediction

DeepMind, the UK-based, Google owned AI research and applications company, has launched DeepMind Health, a subsidiary focused on applying AI to a vast range of healthcare problems. In a five-year deal with the UK's National Health Service, the company has been given access to patient data to develop and deploy its Streams healthcare app. The app will provide doctors and nurses with cell phone alerts about a patient's condition. Applications include spotting people at risk of kidney problems, detecting blood poisoning, and coordinating patient treatment.

In a parallel development, IBM has developed IBM Watson Health, devoted to improving healthcare with cognitive computing. The massive processing power of technologies such as these can revolutionize myriad aspects of healthcare, encompassing diagnosis, care delivery, and management of the patient experience.

Many modern healthcare providers have amassed huge amounts of data on each patient, most of which is unstructured. While today it may take a person weeks to go through reams of patient data, an AI, such as IBM Watson Health, can "read'" 200 pages of information in a second or less. Using powerful processing technology, links can be made between disparate sets of data, old trauma, and previous illnesses. Health and lifestyle information can be interpreted and extrapolated to form an accurate diagnosis in seconds.

Equally, using such processing techniques, an AI can project existing healthcare problems and life style choices into the future. A healthcare AI may be able to warn you about potential problems such as type 2 diabetes, cancer, high blood pressure, and high cholesterol—years before they would normally become apparent.

Drug Development and Clinical Trials

With the cost of genetic testing falling exponentially, and the increase of stratified medicine tailored to our individual genetic make-up, AI can also assist in drug development. Genetic data can be analyzed, extrapolated, and applied to determine the exact chemical composition of drugs required to create individualized medicine. Equally, AI can benefit clinical trials: A mobile phone app called AiCure records people taking their medication, identifying the patient and drug, and deploying sophisticated features such as facial recognition to ensure it is not being tricked. The adherence data is available in real time to organizations conducting clinical trials, ensuring for the first time that they are based on genuine hard data.

Healthcare Management

Applications of AI are already in place in "smart cities," e.g. locality infrastructures designed to inform management decisions on everything from street lighting, to traffic control, and policing. Smart city networks draw on a vast array of sensors and input devices to capture massive amounts of information about populations and their behavior patterns. This Internet of things (IoT) generates huge volumes of data, which are transmitted and shared via cloud computing and interpreted using AI processing capabilities.

As part of the smart city concept, we could see the emergence of smart hospitals. Imagine the medical equipment, beds, and physical fabric of the hospital all providing data about patients, professionals, the building infrastructure, and the logistical flow of people, goods, and health information through the hospital. Which patients have been left unattended for an excessive period? What services are being used the most? How did the infrastructure of the emergency room cope? Where are resources laying idle? Which department is under, or even, over staffed? How can resources and personnel be deployed more effectively?

Using AI, core trends can be monitored in real time and predictions made as to where and when to deploy people and physical resources to maximum benefit. So, for example, if an AI "notices" that the emergency room sees the most heart attacks on Friday afternoons, routine outpatient clinics might be rescheduled away from those times so that extra emergency room doctors and cardiologists can be deployed ahead of time.

Cost and Time Efficiency

Across the healthcare sector as a whole, AI could bring massive efficiency increases. Artificial intelligence chatbots can be trained by and learn from specialists across a range of typical patient and professional interactions. Once in use, the chatbots would deliver advice with the same expertise as a general practitioner and only require human input when previously unseen situations arise.

An AI chatbot can answer questions with more precision and depth than a human probably ever could using patient medical information drawn from multiple sources and combining it with personal data, lifestyle, interests, and hobbies. This can free up a doctor's time to build relationships with patients and focus on the broader aspects of their health and wellbeing.

The UK National Health Service (NHS) has partnered with Babylon Health, a digital healthcare app, to provide an AI-powered chatbot to over 1.2 million patients in North Central London. Patients type in symptoms, the app asks questions to determine severity and advise whether to seek medical assistance, visit a pharmacy, or manage the issue at home. The process typically involves around 12 interactions and takes about 1.5 minutes—less than the time of the average call to the NHS 111 non-emergency helpline. Using AI means diagnosis can be almost instantaneous and comprehensively researched, while stratified medicine can ensure the drugs prescribed for a patient are of genuine benefit.

Ethics, Trust, and Compliance

There is extraordinary and almost limitless potential for AI to change the nature of healthcare delivery, outcomes, and patient wellbeing. Equally it raises new ethical questions and concerns for patients. For example, the predictive power of AI could warn you of heart disease problems that may become apparent many years down the line. For some, this could cause stress if they have not consented to such advanced predictions; furthermore, it may not seem of any importance to their life at this moment. Special attention must be paid to the human side of healthcare in these cases: A process of informed consent, facilitated by a medical counselor, may be necessary to explain the potential insights that an AI may deliver.

Knowing When

For some, an AI chatbot may be viewed an unnatural and untrustworthy patient interface. For example, an older person, less versed in digital technologies, might find it difficult to use and could be unforthcoming in giving it sensitive information about their health problems. This is not just a user service experience problem but also represents an ethical concern: If a patient comes to harm because the doctor's surgery has not provided a service that patients feel comfortable using, then where does the responsibility lie?

On a positive note, an AI chatbot can spend unlimited time listening to the patient's concerns, would act consistently on every occasion, would never get tired, and would be available 24/7/365. Chatbots may be the perfect solution for out of hours' enquiries, housebound individuals, patients in remote places, or those with anxiety about talking to a human. What is critical for healthcare providers is knowing when and where to deploy these AI based healthcare solutions to maximize benefit, minimize harm, and create a sustainable model going forward.

- *What services and health benefits would patients expect in return for sharing their health data?*
- *How should we balance the meddling of AI in our health management with the freedom to choose unhealthy options?*
- *How might society react if AI could one day predict our cause of death with high certainty?*

A version of this article was originally published in *HefMa Pulse Magazine* under the title "Healthcare embraces Artificial Intelligence."

Won't Get Fooled Again: Anticipating Surprises in an Unpredictable Business Environment for Travel, Hospitality, and Business Events

By Rohit Talwar and Alexandra Whittington

How can the travel, hospitality, and business events sectors envision and prepare for the inevitable surprises of the next five years?

In the face of growing global uncertainty, the next five years could bring a dramatic decline as customers cut back on spending plans. Equally, disruptive new technologies, growth in rapidly developing emerging markets, new industry sectors, and the relentless pursuit of business revenues could see the travel industry break all previous records. For the travel, hospitality, and business events sectors, we can get rightly excited about growth opportunities. The difficulty comes when dealing with uncertainty and trying to cater for a range of possible scenarios from boom to global meltdown.

The harsh reality is that change can happen quickly and leave firms in a state of shock, with demand suddenly nosediving because of broader "unforeseen" factors in the business world. So, what are some of the biggest "inevitable surprises" on the horizon that could hit us any time in the next few years, what could they mean for the firms involved, and how can we prepare for them rather than be blindsided when they hit us? This article describes eight surprise developments that will require a timely response from the travel, hospitality, and events world between now and 2023. Is your organization ready?

Many of the top futurists on LinkedIn and Twitter say that they can "future-proof" your business or confer "strategic foresight" to your planning, which will save you from blindly guessing about the future, as your competitors do. The fact is that no futurist—or any other brand advisor, thought-leader or management consultant—can completely eliminate surprises. However, what futurists can teach clients to do is embrace the unpredictability of the current moment and allow imagination and vision to infuse business planning with greater versatility.

Critically, good futurists can impart some of the core skills required to help managers and leaders spot early signs of possible change and prepare for a range of different paths to the future from the present day. As an example of the practical application of future thinking, this chapter will demonstrate how, in the travel and hospitality industries, surprises do not necessarily mean something negative waits around the corner, but can actually open up a series of opportunities for the more agile and innovative businesses.

A surprise can delight us, like an unexpected party thrown in our honor, or it can frighten us, like suddenly happening upon hazardous road conditions while driving. The future will inevitably serve up both pleasant and unpleasant surprises—but spotting individual future developments themselves is not the most critical task for future-focused leaders. Of course, it depends on the nature of the event, but the most important element of a surprise party, or having to suddenly slam on the brakes, is the quality and timeliness of the response. As futurists, our expertise lies in foresight—not in a precise, fortune-telling way, but as a feel for how conditions are changing, as an ability to explore the different possible scenarios that may play out, and as a well-tuned sensitivity to potential fluctuations in key factors shaping the near- and long-term future.

This chapter presents eight of the biggest potential surprises awaiting in the next few years for the travel, hospitality, and meetings sectors. Even though many of these developments might appear to have a touch of sci-fi about them for those who have not had them on their radar, they are all based on solid evidence we have identified in our latest trend and scenario research.

1. The Rise of Surveillance Capitalism

Much favored by the large technology platforms such as Google and Facebook, this is a business model that seeks to provide services intuitively, based on the observed activities, patterns, and preferences of the customer, as determined through analysis of the data they have provided. Each search we do, each posting we make, and each article or cat picture we "like" generates a wealth of information, which can be mined and interpreted using sophisticated big data analysis tools.

Hence, as a way of providing a service, surveillance capitalism rests on the ability to obtain consent to monitor customers. There is growing awareness that consumer-facing businesses with sophisticated technology infrastructures can amass and interpret a scale of big data that allows them to develop intimate knowledge of us as individuals. The concern is that they will then use those insights to manipulate our behavior into making purchase choices. This concept is known as surveillance capitalism.

Almost every business wants to get closer to their customer, and some mistakenly talk about "owning" them—few of us like the idea of being treated as the possession of those we buy goods and services from. The question is how far business should go in pursuit of deeper customer insight? The situation is changing rapidly in two diametrically opposing directions. Firstly, there are numerous tools and technologies which already allow for the immediate capture and analysis of our individual data and for the subsequent generation of personalized customer responses. These include GPS, sensors, mobile, and biometric recognition, artificial intelligence (AI), and predictive analytics.

For example, HSBC bank has implemented ATMs based on facial recognition, while Citi and Barclay's increasingly request voiceprints to identify their customers instantaneously and intuitively. There is an implicit expectation that customers appreciate and benefit from the implied surveillance, and as long as transparency and privacy are prioritized, customers seem willing to use such services. In the next five years, it is possible that personal drones, our online "digital twins," and highly advanced biometrics will be considered essential to providing good customer service. The convenience of voice- or face-based hotel check-out, for example, should strike the right balance between privacy and customization, and avoid the abuse of personal data at all costs.

Concerns over the potential misuse of our data are driving the idea of personal privacy protection. A range of tools are coming to market which would act as intelligent guardians of our data, allowing third parties to only access that which they really need. Such services increasingly question why a meeting organizer or hotel actually needs any of our personal details. A simple numeric identifier could allow us to access the event or a bedroom so long as payment has been made. Such a response to the excesses of surveillance capitalism could seriously undermine the data-centric customer personalization strategies being adopted by many in travel, meetings, and hospitality.

2. Consumerism in Decline?

This potential surprise can be inferred or extrapolated from a range of recent market trends. For example, in the UK, leisure attraction manager Merlin Entertainments has reported a decline in visitor numbers—while the operator of Legoland, the London Eye, and Madame Tussauds attributes some of the decline to recent terror attacks, the bulk is due to longer term tourism trends. In the US, previously stable restaurant chains like Applebee's are failing, while malls and retail are in general decline, with up to 1,000 stores closing each week and a massive wave of closures executed in 2017 by the likes of Gymboree, Radio Shack, Macy's, JCPenney, Sears, and Kmart. The closures are not fully covered by increased online sales. In response, analysts and investors are beginning to wonder if encouraging consumerism is perhaps no longer a panacea for a slumping economy.

In part, the trend may be driven by a movement away from ownership towards usership, and a growing preference for experiences over physical goods. However, perhaps a bigger phenomenon is the relative demise in the spending power of the middle classes in many mature economies such as the US and the UK. This relative middle class decline has, in many ways, set the stage for a movement away from consumerism and toward frugalism.

Furthermore, today's Western Millennials are increasingly characterized as dragged down by debt, constrained by low or no wage growth, concerned over poor job stability, and often left with little disposable income. A simple lack of demand is a key driver of this trend. Another driving force is increasing awareness of the impact of constant consumption on fragile ecological systems. Even when conscious consumers buy, they are doing so sparingly.

The sharing economy is a perfect example of young consumers rejecting mass consumption patterns. There are a number of examples emerging which show how a new generation has eschewed the obsession with ownership, such as co-living, where numerous unrelated individuals share a home in dorm-like settings. Others include the popularity of community resource sharing schemes like Streetbank, and ride sharing, which negates the need to own a car.

For the tourism sector, Airbnb room sharing is a demonstration of how new consumers have rejected exclusivity and the trappings of hotels in favor of modest or practical rooms. In particular, Airbnb speaks to the focus of this consumer segment on experiences over materialism—thus the attractions and services of a hotel can pale in comparison to the potentially authentic experience that a guest room in a private home offers. Being able to cater to this type of consumer, particularly at the same time that the luxury contingent continues to be served, is a surprise development many hospitality outlets may not anticipate as key to competitive survival over the next few years. For the meetings sector, this trend towards cost saving, frugality, and a rejection of the apparently lavish or ostentatious could have a direct impact on delegate willingness to attend events, and their resulting expectations if they do.

3. Artificial Intelligence

A prime contender for the hottest and most hyped technology of the 21st century, AI is penetrating every business sector and laying the foundations for a revolution in the delivery of products and services. We have been using AI for some time in smartphones, aircraft auto-pilots, GPS, and credit scoring software. The range of applications is now set to explode over the next 18 months. For example, new models like Amazon's My Mix provide an algorithm to serve as an intelligent personal shopper, suggesting items and curating them like a Pinterest page.

Clearly, it will not be long before companies offer customized shipments of items we might like, because their AI knows our shopping and lifestyle habits. This information will typically be gleaned from analysis of our online behavior and from interactions with the intelligent agents that manage and monitor our lives via our smart mobile devices. The effect would be that subscription boxes become predictive, so that apparently unspoken consumer preferences are seamlessly guiding a range of service and product providers that anticipate, rather than meet, our needs.

In tourism and hospitality, a customer's preferences for products, services, and desired levels of engagement with humans could be gauged, predicted, and catered for before they arrive at a hotel, for example. Imagine a hotel room stocked with all your favorite toiletries and mini-bar snacks, the right number of towels, and pillows fluffed to the appropriate density. Whether our requirements are met via AI or the human touch, the capacity or inability to personalize with such premium perks could enhance or damage the reputation of a hospitality business. Furthermore, automation can provide specialized moments of customer engagement—such as the perfect choice of fragrances, teas, colors, and dynamically changing electronic wall-paper displays—that hopefully strengthen the relationship.

4. Political Uncertainty

Politics has re-emerged from the shadow of global business—recapturing the media spotlight and engulfing the globe—with unpredictability as the essence of all conceivable geopolitical futures. It is important to consider the impact on destinations: Are we on the verge of experiencing a Brexit/Trump/North Korea/ISIS effect? Could a situation arise where isolationism, terrorism, and hostile political and economic conditions could deter customers from doing business in certain locations? Political uncertainty can paralyze planning, financially, and in terms of company morale.

While some worry that Brexit might drive businesses and visitors away from the UK, there are also policy changes in the US that are expected to deter international visitors to conferences and events. These moves could also lead to some businesses moving offshore to make it easier for their foreign staff to function effectively. Strict travel regulations put the hospitality industry in the middle of a potentially chaotic situation. It may become important for hotels to provide a calm oasis away from the stressful, dangerous, and potentially invasive world of international travel, particularly for meetings that bring participants from all over the world.

Heightened geo-political awareness is of particular importance given the constant flow of projections that suggest that future growth in traveler numbers is likely to come from China, as well as those who practice Islam. These regional shifts in dominant traveler profiles mean that, to stay competitive, the meetings and hospitality sectors will need to take their game to the next level in terms of language skills and cultural sensitivity, encompassing diet, religion, protocols, customs, and practices. However, with the rise of nationalism and increased hostility towards "the other" in some quarters, attempts to cater for certain traveler groups by displaying heightened cultural sensitivity could also be perceived as a controversial and unpatriotic gesture.

5. Retail on the Road

A development that might surprise the hotel industry is seeing cars become a shopping venue. We've witnessed the rise of Uber as a new model for thinking about transportation; an entire generation has awakened to the fact that it is not that a car you need, but a ride with a customer-centric booking process. The next evolution will be self-driving taxis and other autonomous vehicles, even potentially personal drones and flying cars. Such an "inevitable surprise" could create newfound chunks of time for companies to interact commercially with people riding in connected cabs and self-driving cars.

Car-sharing and taxi app services free up time for consumers to shop when they would normally be driving (or parking) personal cars. Furthermore, free of fixed transportation expenses and significant differences in the average consumer's disposable income could be on the horizon. Hospitality can certainly benefit from the funds normally used to purchase a car, gasoline, and insurance suddenly being freed up for travel or room stays and recreational activities in hotels.

6. Digital Currency

A growing number of businesses are now accepting digital currencies and the most prominent among them—Bitcoin and Ether—have seen recent price spikes followed by significant reversals. At the time of writing, Bitcoin is valued at US$18,000 per coin, giving it a market capitalization of US$305 billion, surpassing that of VISA. The next biggest is Ethereum with a market capitalization of US$42 billion.

Bitcoin, Ether, and the other digital currencies offer completely new systems for payments, reservations, and billing that the hospitality industry can benefit from. The basic mechanism bypasses traditional centralized financial clearing and accounting systems and their associated charges. The model enables direct financial flows between buyer and seller with the transaction captured in a distributed and highly encoded, and hence, theoretically immutable ledger of record. So, while the Bitcoin exchanges might get hacked, the transactions records are there as an unchangeable matter of permanent record.

There are larger numbers of Bitcoin owners than ever, and with the current economic uncertainties surrounding banking and finance, there is good reason to think the popularity of digital currencies will continue to grow. The rising adoption of these alternatives to credit cards and cash will require firms to develop new technological capacities around the sales of products and services.

Hotels and meetings will need to cater for customers using digital currency wallets, for example. The fact that most reservation systems are based on credit cards suggests this could be a difficult hurdle. Is it possible to imagine holding a room with Bitcoin? A key twist here is the recognition that blockchain, the decentralized ledger that forms the public database of digital currency transactions, can be used for information transfer activities beyond payments and money transfers.

7. Blockchain

There is so much more to digital currencies than just payments. Indeed, over time, blockchain-based contracts could completely automate the reservation process and be applied to a number of other functions including delivery management, ordering, accounting, and record keeping. Self-executing contracts, also known as "smart contracts," could revolutionize the monitoring of and payment of service provider obligations and reduce the accounts payable workload (and hence workforce) considerably. As an instant and irrefutable record of transactions, blockchain might serve well for tracking room charges and in-room purchases.

Blockchains can be used to track payments, and can also be applied to confirm inventory, validate documents, verify ownership, and notarize the authenticity of a variety of things. For example, Dubai International Airport is pioneering the use of blockchain for digital passports and others are applying them for everything from verification of academic credentials to the tracking of artworks.

The versatility of blockchain in the hotel and meetings accommodations sector could bring major benefits and cause significant disruption, as it stands to impact the workforce most dramatically.

Going a step further, with the amount of blockchain and AI development taking place in the financial and technology sectors today, it's possible that some organizations could be run entirely on algorithms and blockchain within five years. Such distributed autonomous organizations (DAOs) exist only in the form of software and have literally no employees.

8. Immersive Technologies

Cutting-edge immersive visual technologies like augmented reality (AR) and virtual reality (VR) and shared mobile video content could have a major impact on meetings and hospitality. The ability to record and enhance a range of experiences might compete directly with live meetings and hospitality in the sense that in-company meetings are increasingly virtual and teams, more and more, work remotely.

Whilst there is always likely to be a space for live events, immersive technology will increasingly encroach on the sector's territory. Evolving from today's social media, digitally shared video and experiences may constitute the future of many social interactions including work but extending to weddings, family reunions, and other celebrations.

With augmented offerings, it's not just the visual senses being tempted; soon, brain-computer interfaces could simulate touch, taste, and smell sensations as well. Eventually, digital experiences of food, travel, and even sex could compete with real-life in terms of authenticity and satisfaction. Strong, convincing simulations are something for the hotel world to consider.

Technologies that can create authentic, shared experiences could increasingly become a lower-cost alternative for how people gather in the next five years. If hospitality and meeting providers can utilize these technologies in ways that emphasize the human element, they may find new opportunities for preserving what matters when it comes to meetings and physical travel experiences.

Enhanced awareness of these potential surprises can ensure a timely and effective response, but obviously not everyone outside of the futurist profession knows where and how to look for early signals of surprises on the horizon. Most futurists have a daily practice that involves extensive reading and information gathering on emerging developments, a process known as "horizon scanning."

Scanning is a research technique that can be applied in any organization; it basically involves building up a wide range of sources of reading material to gain a number of unique, differing, and possibly fringe perspectives on current events, technological developments, and economics, for instance. The information might come from a Twitter feed, a Google alert, or some other form of regularly updated information such as a Facebook group.

Many businesses may feel they cannot devote the time to scanning that a professional futurist might. However, even encouraging staff to allocate five minutes a day to the process can start to build an increasingly rich and diverse set of perspectives on possible changes on the horizon. The important thing is to build a diversity of voices into your organization's daily information diet.

Diversifying information sources is critical for identifying new developments and growing the "anticipation muscle." Most importantly, tapping into diverse sources ensures you are attuned to a spectrum of emergent potential surprises in your industry and the broader business environment. Learning to anticipate the future with imagination and an open mind may be the best "future-proofing" money can't buy.

- *How could travel sector businesses exploit their wealth of accumulated personal data without overstepping customers' boundaries?*

- *What opportunities may arise from the combinatorial effect of these inevitable surprises?*

- *How might businesses embrace uncertainty and infuse versatility into their planning and strategy processes?*

A version of this article was originally published under the title "Won't Get Fooled Again: Anticipating Surprises in an Unpredictable Business Environment for Travel, Hospitality and Business Events."

Authenticating the Travel Experience with Blockchain

By Rohit Talwar, Alexandra Whittington, April Koury, Steve Wells, and Maria Romero

How might blockchain technology enhance trust and authenticity in the travel experience?

In today's travel industry, authenticity has become a powerful draw. Travelers increasingly want authentic experiences—providing cultural insights while avoiding mass travel packages. Authenticity embraces honest advertising and customer experience, factors that industry providers have total control over. Now, there is a high-tech disruptor emerging that could help travel industry businesses offer greater authenticity and share the benefits with customers in numerous ways: blockchain.

Blockchain is the transaction tracking platform for Bitcoin, the leading digital cryptocurrency. Blockchain is a secure public ledger that that can capture and encode all transactions in any given currency and a range of other types of information such as traveler details. Globally, numerous cryptocurrencies are available, each with its own blockchain.

In the future, some or all nations may have their own digital currency; however, the borderless cryptocurrency concept rather defies notions of nation-states, sovereign currencies, and centralized banks. Imagine travelers unburdened by exchange rates or bank fees and providers accepting payment from anyone who has a digital wallet. At the philosophical level, blockchainS and cryptocurrencies embody a rebellion against intermediaries like banks and credit card companies.

Payments are the most obvious and immediate travel application, and progressive vendors aware of blockchain's potential are beginning to accept cryptocurrency payments. From a purist's perspective, a blockchain renders banks unnecessary middlemen—speeding "peer-to-peer" payments between buyer and seller.

Eventually, blockchains could enable entirely new forms of value, e.g. future cash alternatives could be invented and tracked on blockchains, including "sharing" points earned on social media sites, credits for community involvement (e.g. after school tutoring), or rewards for contributing to neighborhood recycling, sustainability, and conservation efforts. Just as hotel and taxi operators ignored the disruptive and costly impact of simple customer-centric apps like Uber and Airbnb, could blockchain weave new and unnoticed threats into the tourism ecosystem?

The tourism industry is increasingly basing growth strategies on personalization—loyalty schemes and targeted marketing programs that rely on knowing the individual's identity. However, a blockchain protects personal identity, anonymizing users, enforcing secure validation, and making identity theft impossible. Whilst immigration authorities would still need proof of identity, the rest of the industry value chain might only know of you as authorized traveler #6759704.

On perhaps a more positive note, blockchain customer validation could diminish queues and wait times as a lot of the processing could take place in transit. Over time, travelers could also regain a feeling of anonymity and freedom, rather than one of being surveilled, tracked, and owned. If we can link the human in front of us to their unique blockchain profile (possibly through biometrics), all other ID checks become irrelevant.

If we choose, our blockchain personal identities could contain more than just passport information—preferences could be shared during the trip, so every service along the journey can be uniquely tailored without ever knowing our name unless we provide it. For providers, the consequences of a cyberattack are greatly diminished as the underlying customer data is anonymized and secure.

Blockchain is poised to have a potentially dramatic impact on travel in the next 5 to 10 years. Blockchain could disrupt every step of the industry value chain by mainstreaming alternative currencies, securing irrefutable identities, reducing transaction costs, and challenging current marketing thinking. Indeed, blockchains, coupled with other exponentially accelerating technologies like artificial intelligence, cloud computing, hyperconnectivity, and the Internet of things, could transform society.

The challenge for travel sector leaders is to ensure that their organization has deep and widespread understanding of the nature of these new technologies and the previously unimaginable travel concepts, service offerings, business models, operational challenges, and strategic options they could enable. At the heart of the challenge is digital literacy and the mindset change that goes with it. Within twelve months we'll be bored of talking about the need for mindset change—best to get a head start.

- *What might be the biggest impacts of blockchain for the travel industry when coupled with other potentially disruptive technologies like artificial intelligence or the Internet of things?*

- *How might blockchain affect the travel industry's marketing strategies going forward?*

- *As customers, under what circumstances would we want to share our personal data if we didn't need to?*

A version of this article was originally published in *Travolution* under the title "Authenticating the Travel Experience."

Exploring the Future of Automotive in a World of Disruption

By Rohit Talwar and Alexandra Whittington

What are the critical themes that leaders in automotive and road transport management must wrestle with as they develop future strategies?

Developing Future-Aware and Connected Leaders

Tomorrow's leaders in the automotive sector will face an unprecedented range of changes and challenges to navigate as they steer the organization's path into the future. When those in road transport management look to leaders in the automotive sector for answers, we realize that they are so deep in the "I don't know" stage of industry evolution that they cannot offer the clarity the former are seeking. Hence both sets of leaders need to be deeply connected to the world around them to ensure they are truly aware of potentially disruptive current and emerging developments taking place across the sectors and in the broader environment.

However, as we look to 2040 and beyond, there are few facts about what has yet to happen. In many cases, it is far too early to distinguish between what could turn out to be temporary fads and the more substantive ideas and developments that could turn into significant trends that will have a meaningful impact on the sector.

With an accelerating pace of change, developments can emerge, grow exponentially, and have a significant disruptive impact in a very short space of time. We cannot simply sit back and wait to see what might happen. As industry leaders, we need to ensure we are developing our anticipatory skills, scanning the horizon for signs of future change, and building the ability to act fast in evaluating and responding to the resulting future insights.

Good foresight has become a critical tool for conscious leaders. It equips us to make our own choices about how best to take advantage of emerging opportunities and protect against potential threats. Across every part of the automotive and road transport infrastructure value chains, we are witnessing a number of these developments and emerging ideas which need to be understood.

In the absence of hard facts, we have explored the ambiguous nature of these six forces to outline possible scenarios that, while low on certainty, would have a large impact on the automotive industry and, in turn, the highways management sector. These address the themes of:

- Concept to Production
- Digital and Connected
- Autonomous Vehicles
- Evolution of Business Models
- Societal Shifts, and
- Rapidly Evolving Markets.

Here's a glimpse of the future of automobiles: What we might see, why we might see it, and when.

From Concept to Production

Nanotechnology, smart materials, and a range of new and emerging design and manufacturing approaches are starting to enter the automotive and road maintenance sectors. These could have a significant potential impact on the value chain from concept creation and vehicle design through to manufacturing, maintenance, and repair by 2020. These will offer super-aerodynamic automobile designs from highly flexible, cost-efficient, and easy to maintain new materials.

Boeing has introduced a new metal that's touted as being "light as air," for example. Lighter vehicles can be more efficient, and stronger—in this case, thanks to a design made of tubes thinner than a hair that mimics human bone structure. The material can absorb tremendous shock despite its delicate composition. Superior strength and efficiency could deliver cost savings across the entire value chain.

The car industry is accelerating the use of 3D printing as a strategy for saving time and money in producing prototypes, components, and entire cars. For example, Local Motors is using 3D printing to develop entirely new vehicle lines such as the Strati which has just 50 components. This also offers the potential to reduce transportation costs and repair time by 3D printing spare parts on site. There may come a time when it is cheaper to print, rather than fix, a part or vehicle.

3D printing could also allow us to reintroduce iconic vehicle designs of the past and manufacture them economically in very small quantities. In the medium to longer term, 4D printing could enable us to produce objects that can change their shape and properties over time. To avoid junkyards full of 3D printed scrap, the car industry is also increasingly focused on reusable or recyclable materials.

Digital and Connected

Digital transformation, the Internet of things (IoT), and advances in smart technologies such as robotics and artificial intelligence (AI) are blurring the boundary between the physical and virtual world. In fact, by 2025, we can anticipate vehicles using these and other cutting edge technologies such as hyperconnectivity, blockchain, cloud computing, and drones to help drivers accomplish goals other than driving. Collectively, they could turn our cars into always on, highly connected, self-monitoring, self-managing technology platforms that can be updated as frequently as the app library on a mobile phone, so much so that more than 80% of the value of vehicles is expected to lie in their digital components by 2040.

Not only are vehicles becoming smart, autonomous, and communicative, but they are starting to combine multiple emerging technologies. Could automobiles become new spaces for conducting other business besides transportation? For example, manufacturers and resellers are looking at adding constantly updated flexible external display panels to cars to generate advertising revenues for the owners.

Ford is using drones to guide self-driving cars, so these vehicles can operate when there's no internet service—taking autonomous vehicles beyond the city limits. Similarly, Local Motors has a car design equipped to launch a drone, which provides the driver with a bird's-eye view of the landscape. Indeed, many of the advances coming into our cars will help recreate the automobile's heyday when a Sunday drive might provide a few hours' entertainment.

Autonomous Vehicles

A growing number of manufacturers are building fully or partially autonomous vehicles. Dramatic claims are being made about their potential to cut accident rates, improve fuel management, increase traffic flows, and reduce the number of taxis required in a city. As we move from partially to fully autonomous vehicles, by 2040 we could reach a point where all new vehicles and existing stock must be retrofitted with a self-driving mode. This could see human drivers criminalized, ostracized, or otherwise considered deviant members of society with driving becoming an anachronism.

Every manufacturer and a range of new entrants are pursuing the autonomous dream. Uber is planning a fleet of self-driving cars, with live trials in Pittsburgh and another recently halted in California, while its Otto subsidiary has powered the first autonomous truck. There's already a self-driving minivan, a self-steering cruise ship, and self-flying planes. There are also self-flying cars and single person drones. Key goals here are lower accident rates, more efficient traffic flows, lower emissions, reduced car parking requirements, and shorter journey times.

The most drastic possible expression of the autonomous vehicle revolution sees a world in which human drivers are considered too dangerous, unpredictable, distractible, and probably uninsurable. A shift to completely self-driving vehicles would require a campaign to recast driving as the new smoking or the new drunk driving. However, while this likely to be unpopular with many drivers, like those other campaigns, such changes might ultimately be a good thing for society as a whole.

Yet, nostalgia is a difficult obstacle to overcome. The rise of the automobile played a large part in creating specialty facets of modern culture: car hobbyists, suburban communities, and road trips, to name a few, and these would not be possible without automobiles. Some people alive today grew up during this automobile revolution, and it plays a role in their personal identity. Now, some of those same Baby Boomers and GenXers may experience the emergence of a diametrically opposite worldview: humanity unfit to operate a car. Ultimately, it is possible that driving could become little more than a sentimental artefact of the post-World War II era.

Evolution of Business Models

There is gradual shift taking place from focusing on a vehicle as a one-off product sale to viewing it as a digital service platform, information center, and commercial portal with recurring revenue streams. At the same time, consumers are embracing concepts like the sharing economy with a growing interest in "usership" over ownership. Hence, a number of manufacturers now offer shared ownership schemes. Car sharing is possibly the most widespread new model with anywhere from 6 to 40 people sharing ownership of a single vehicle. This clearly has an impact on automotive sales revenues and maintenance costs as each vehicle is used anywhere from 5 to 50 times more than under single ownership.

For many, the rise of taxi services like Uber has enabled them to see their car as a revenue earning asset, not a cost center. This creates opportunities for manufacturers to explore the potential of sharing risks and rewards with the vehicle owner. Some are going so far as to suggest that by 2030 we could see the emergence of "self-owning" autonomous vehicles operating as taxis 24 hours a day, seven days a week. The idea is that those involved in producing the vehicle, supplying the components, refueling it, and servicing it would receive a continuous stream of revenues from the earnings of the vehicle over its lifetime.

Consumers also see opportunities for vehicle ownership to increase their income as well. By 2020, it could be common for vehicles to produce a paycheck rather than eat into it. Uber and Airbnb have normalized the idea of using personal possessions to make money, and that's exactly what future car consumers might also sense: What they drive is not just a car, but an underutilized ATM. Peer-to-peer car lending via Turo, FlightCar, and other such platforms already started moving beyond the fringe in 2017. The idea of renting out your car when not driving it may mesh well with the gig economy, as a way to enhance income—or to simply justify vehicle ownership at all.

Within the industry, BMW and Toyota have introduced technologies that are enabling the re-use of electric vehicle batteries to charge the home. Elsewhere researchers have tested cars that charge while driving on specialized "smart" roads. These developments are budget-friendly, but are also bringing drivers one step closer to becoming energy producers rather than just consumers. Any vehicular advances that promote off-grid use, or generate and capture solar, kinetic, or any type of energy, are potential money-makers. Fascinating new business models could share the revenue from the energy generated from smart roads between all the players in the ecosystem by 2040.

Societal Shifts

A number of broader societal trends are also beginning to touch on the automotive world. Again, their long-term impact is very difficult to predict, and so we have to prepare for a range of possibilities. For example, we are experiencing radical changes in public thinking about the need for more integrated planning of the future of mobility and the value of smart infrastructures. The expectation is that transport systems and city infrastructures can be managed far better with lower ecological impact once the fully connected vehicle is communicating continuously with its external environment.

At the same time, a variety of "open source" car design projects such as OSVehicle, coupled with the reduced complexity of 3D printed cars and electric vehicles, are bringing down the cost and time to develop new designs. There is also growing societal acceptance of crowdfunding platforms like Kickstarter for innovation and Crowd Cube for raising equity.

Collectively, these societal shifts are enabling new vehicle manufacturers to test the market for new product concepts and raise seed funding without making major initial investments. The crowdfunding platforms are proving an effective route to raise finance and build brand awareness amongst a target market. A growing societal emphasis on environmental sustainability is also spurring the development of green vehicles and encouraging manufacturers to think about recycling and the "cradle-to-cradle" lifecycle of a vehicle.

We are experiencing radical changes in public thinking about the need for more integrated planning of future mobility with lower ecological impacts. By 2040 specific, regional, and local needs could displace "Big Automotive's" monopoly, with cars designed locally using open source platforms such as OSCar—targeted at local residents based on usage patterns made evident via big data.

A major driver of future infrastructure is the smart city. All over the world, cities see the advantage of capturing data from every corner to run the city more efficiently and safely. Alongside these benefits there are also many risks, such as loss of individual free will and privacy. A major consideration in smart city planning is the balance between housing, industry, parking, and transportation, and that's where cars come in.

By 2040, it's possible to imagine that future smart cities will adopt very specific types of transportation technologies and approaches that best suit their specialized needs. Some will rely on autonomous cars while others may prioritize renewable fuel vehicles instead. Some may opt for both. Behavior modification around congestion, traffic, and driving in general are among a smart city's key strategies.

Localized solutions to transportation may be preferred in some cases, particularly if there are ecological, political, or cultural reasons for a smart city choosing, say, large-scale public transportation over individual cars. Because big data is the key here, future smart cities will be automated to the hilt, and all decisions will be made based on what needs their particular data reveals.

Rapidly Evolving Markets

The rapid development and sizeable populations of many emerging countries are creating new vehicle markets, and several million new car buyers enter the market each year. From ultra-lost cost vehicles such as the Tata Nano through to extreme luxury, demand is growing. Competition is also likely to increase as local manufacturers continue to emerge in more populous countries such as China, India, Malaysia, and Indonesia.

Today, in contrast to the developed world, emerging economies largely reject car sharing or self-driving vehicles and fully embrace the idea of individual car ownership. However, by 2030, advanced technologies should make it possible to leapfrog toward sustainable transportation, thus electric vehicles (EVs), renewables, and biofuels could well be prioritized. The demand for ecologically sound cars could reach a frenzy.

Whether BRICs (Brazil, Russia, India, China), MINTs (Mexico, Indonesia, Nigeria, Turkey), or TICKs (Taiwan, India, China, Korea), the emerging world economies are where it's at for all kinds of consumer goods, from refrigerators to air conditioners. However, the emerging economies of today can learn from the mistakes more industrialized countries have made. Many are gradually embracing the sustainable option—with some seeing the commercial potential. In fact, the developing world leads in the consumption of renewable energy, with Bangladesh, for example, being one of the worlds' biggest markets for solar home systems.

Developing countries able to implement the right financial incentives may find that EVs ride the demand explosion for renewable energy. Currently, Renault has plans to roll out an inexpensive EV for China, which is where demand for EVs is expected to grow most. On the other end of the consumer spectrum, Jaguar Land Rover wants to station an EV hub in the UK. In the future, the leading economies—new and old—might need alternatives to fossil fuels, and the EV is one of the leading adaptations maturing societies have to choose from when it comes to using resources efficiently and cost effectively.

The Broader Global Context

These industry-level forces are also at play in the broader economy, where they are combining with a general thrust towards increased globalization, rapidly evolving economies, digital transformation, shorter and faster business cycles, and the rise of cyber currencies. In this broader context, questions are being raised about major issues such as:

- The role and purpose of business in tomorrow's society,
- The impact of automation on future employment opportunities,
- How to educate tomorrow's workers and citizens? and,
- The implications of global markets and disruptive technological shifts on national identity, values, and governance.

A Future-Conscious Approach to Leadership Development

So, collectively, these forces of change are driving uncertainty—and fueling disruption, renewal, and transformation in every sector. In response to this "perfect storm" of change on the horizon, the automotive sector is being challenged to think hard about future strategies and how to respond to these forces both individually and through their collective impact. For both the automotive and Smart Highway sectors, the first priority has to be developing an effective "horizon scanning" function to identify and analyze the emerging changes and explore the alternative possible scenarios and their implications. Whilst the sectors may be able to influence each other's decision making, a more reliable approach would be to prepare for a range of possible scenarios as hope is not a strategy.

For both sectors, new "conscious leadership" perspectives are required on how to deal with disruptive news entrants, how to innovate in design, manufacturing, and distribution, how to evolve business models and organization designs, and how to ensure effective stakeholder engagement in a fast changing world.

These transformative challenges are in turn raising fundamental questions on the future nature and capabilities required of leadership, and how to attract, develop, and retain the type of talent needed across the organization to ensure future relevance and growth. Our experience is that the best managed organizations are aiming to develop leaders who are prepared for a broad range of possible developments, opportunities, and challenges, and who are conscious of the different possible scenarios through which they may play out. We find that this deep sense of future orientation helps unlock the leadership drive, imagination, and personal capacity required to create a positive future for the organization.

Next generation leadership programs will need to explore a range of these emerging developments and the questions they will raise for tomorrow's leaders. They should examine possible scenarios for how these developments might combine and play out. Finally, they need to generate and prioritize ideas on practical next steps to exploring the horizon and embedding future awareness in the toolkit of tomorrow's conscious leader.

- *How might automakers, smart city leaders, transport planners, and citizens work together to develop workable solutions for the autonomous era?*
- *How might these forces of change impact related sectors like the automotive aftermarket?*

Versions of this article were originally published in *GQ Magazine* and in *Smart Highways Magazine*.

Follow the Money –
The Future Evolution of
Automotive Markets

By Rohit Talwar and Alexandra Whittington

How might a deep focus on customer-centricity revolutionize the automotive sector?

The automotive industry is undergoing a period of rapid and radical transformation fueled by a range of technological innovations, digital advancements, and wave after wave of new entrants and alternative business models; as a result, the entire sector is seeing major disruption. Here we highlight the key drivers of change for the sector and explore possible outcomes in such a rapidly evolving market.

Rise of the Sharing Economy

The sharing economy is transforming transportation in several unexpected ways. Uber, probably the best-known example, has its own unique ecosystem of passengers, drivers, and car owners. It has shown itself to be revolutionary enough to disrupt the taxicab system worldwide. Uber brought about this disruption without owning a single vehicle or—until recently—employing a single driver; instead, it has achieved a valuation of around US$68 billion through the magic of smart phones.

The Uber story goes to show that a car is no longer just a thing to drive, but a service that meets the needs of consumers who've been priced out of ownership or prefer on-demand use of transportation. Today, a car is a potential source of passive income for its owner, and a flexible asset for the start-up companies that would like to be middlemen in the continuum from car ownership through to car ride services based on "usership." Where we once talked of selling or leasing to an individual, cars in a shared ownership scheme typically have anywhere from 6 to 40 joint owners or lessees.

Sharing models reduce the cost of ownership for the individual but can dramatically increase the level of usage, the rate of wear and tear, and the servicing costs for the warranty provider. Over time we might see smart data services emerge that draw on the mass of sensor data coming from the car to profile each individual's usage of the vehicle and charge them accordingly. Where the vehicle is provided on a shared lease basis to the user pool, then the costs to the fleet owner can rise because of this potentially dramatic increase in usage rates of each car.

Smart Device Revolution

There are a number of ways innovative new companies are hoping to help the automotive sector adapt to the needs of the emerging transport consumer. Business models are embracing at least three consumer priorities when it comes to using a car: driving, owning, and sharing. And it just so happens that these three priorities are best coordinated via smartphone, a mega-trend transforming business and industry across the globe.

In India, for example, where an on-demand car economy is thriving, Zoomcar, Myles, and Revv are three notable start-ups hoping to change the car driving ecosystem. These rental fleets seek privately-owned cars to place in service for customers to rent while the owners are not using them. So rather than pay fares to ride in someone else's vehicle (as with Uber), Zoomcar lets drivers rent and operate someone else's personal car, allowing Zoomcar to keep its inventory low and maximize profits.

Start-ups like these may be involved in the loan contracts for independent owners to purchase new cars specifically for the purpose of leasing them out for extra income. As a new business model, sharing means multi-stakeholder automobile purchases enter the mainstream. The decision base for consumers' transportation options is growing wider. For example, consumers may opt for larger cargo space or bigger passenger seating areas depending on what they can earn from leasing different types of vehicles. Their purchase considerations may involve not only their own needs, but also the potential to profit from the product they are purchasing.

The model, if proven, could start to create interesting alternative options for more traditional fleet owners and car rental firms. A sufficiently large pool size should ensure availability on demand, reduce capital investment, and lower ownership costs as a result of transferring these to the car owners. More creative schemes might include shared or fractional ownership of private vehicles in return for a guaranteed level of access. Equally it could generate additional potential revenues for fleet owners and individual drivers if their vehicles could be rented out when not in use.

Differentiated Automotive - Mobilize the Fleet

The question arises: Why be limited to just one type of automobile? There is a growing on-demand car audience being served through the "car club subscription" service model of ownership offered by the likes of YoYo and Clutch. Rather than purchase, or lease, a single car, this type of program entitles the member to the use of a car, or fleet of cars, as needed. In this scenario, the driver could choose an SUV for shopping and a sports car for weekend road trips. There is little need to commit to a single car if you do not want to. With limited access for anyone not living in large urban areas, partial or shared car ownership may become a symbol of cosmopolitan living, like a subway pass or bus card.

For those who wish to continue the traditional car-owning experience, the choices for shopping and finance will be as varied as the design and engine options available to them. Automotive e-commerce, like car design itself, is experiencing a renaissance, with players like Roadster, Beepi, and Carvana re-defining the car-buying experience online. These are deal-oriented websites selling cars, supported by brick-and-mortar outlets, but with a mission to put to rest the imagery of wheeling and dealing with salesmen on car lots.

The Connected Car

As we see an increasing level of electronic functionality in the "always on" vehicle, so the nature of the business model changes—with the potential for new revenue streams to emerge. The bigger the installed base of connected car owners we serve, the broader the range of services we can offer. Opportunities range from securing discounts through aggregated buying of fuel, to directing the driver to a specific repair garage when the sensors detect the tires or brakes need replacing. Aggregating the data collected from sensor-rich vehicles will also enable the creation of a range of new information products that might become a valuable revenue stream over time.

The advent of thin film display screens will allow us to charge advertisers to display dynamically updated promotions on the external surfaces of the car. The advertisements might change regularly as we drive through neighborhoods with varying citizen demographics and wealth profiles. A number of players could act as the electronic service provider here, taking a range of income streams from the various activities.

Consumer Trends

A growing number of automotive sector start-ups recognize that the modern car consumer is educated, comparison-oriented, savvy, and knows what they want. While it may sound like a luxury service, the future of car buying online is expected to be highly practical, and designed for the time-poor car buyer. The new automotive e-commerce looks a lot more like Amazon than personal shopping in a department store; Carvana, for instance, has used glass storage towers of cars to cultivate its image of selling cars by "vending machine." The new online car vending approach seeks to replicate a shopping app: Select, purchase, and receive your new car from a warehouse in a simple, fast, and seamless experience.

With all these emerging options, vehicle financiers need to think about how the flows of money through the system are changing and how to make the most of opportunities available to potential customers. They will need to decide whether to take on the risks that come with acknowledging they have little influence over what consumers decide to buy, and no control over what the consumers actually do with the final product.

The sharing economy is all about decentralization, something that is made more and more feasible as smart phones, for example, assist consumers in obtaining their precise wants and needs. It's time to recognize that customers are taking back power that used to belong to the banks, the manufacturers, and the dealers, and they're using the technologies in the palm of their hand to do it.

- *What strategies might traditional companies adopt in order to win in the face of the wave of disruptive changes on the horizon?*
- *As more accessible exponential technologies democratize driving, owning, and sharing, what broader impacts could these changes have on society?*
- *What new business models might emerge around the use and ownership of vehicles?*

A version of this article was originally published in *Asset Finance International* under the title "Follow the Money – The Future Evolution of Automotive Markets."

AI and the Legal Sector: Gift Bearing Friend or Havoc-Wreaking Foe?

By Rohit Talwar and Steve Wells

How might law firms harness the transformational potential of technological change to drive exponential business growth?

We are at the start of a Fourth Industrial Revolution—a wave of transformation fueled by powerful technologies such as artificial intelligence (AI). This could drive a bigger wave of growth in the legal sector than any other change in history. Previous transformations gave us steam-based mechanization, electrification and mass production, and then electronics, information technology, and automation. This new era of smart machines is fueled by exponential improvement and convergence of multiple scientific and technological fields.

So, what is AI? Artificial intelligence is a computer science discipline that seeks to create intelligent machines that can replicate critical human mental faculties. Key applications include speech recognition, language translation, visual perception, learning, reasoning, inference, strategy formation, planning, decision-making, and intuition. The truly transformational impacts arise when AI is combined with accelerating science and technology developments in other fields, including neuroscience, large-scale databases, super-computing hardware, network communications, cloud computing, hyperconnectivity, blockchain distributed ledger systems, the Internet of things, 3D and 4D printing, and digital currencies.

These technologies will transform old industries and accelerate the creation of new ones. All this will generate massive opportunities for law firms, particularly in the corporate sector. However, some lawyers see AI and the technologies it enables as an existential threat to a US$650 billion global industry. They worry about automating their own knowledge, expertise, and advice-based roles. They are particularly concerned about the resultant risks of eliminating differentiation, commoditizing premium revenue streams, losing out to technology providers, depersonalization, and the loss of professional jobs.

While these risks are real, a growing number can smell opportunity, realizing that these technologies will transform the US$75 trillion global economy. By 2025, in a global economy of around US$120 trillion, over half of it will arise from newborn sectors and those that don't even exist today—such as synthetic energy, autonomous vehicles, self-replicating machines, and adaptive, self-repairing materials. In most cases, we haven't started to assess the legal implications—and that means opportunity.

What happens when each industry in every country has its "Uber moment"? Ambitious upstarts are, or soon will be, challenging long-established norms and unspoken rules of engagement in every industry. This creates massive opportunities for law firms, whether by representing the innovators, their adversaries, or the regulators.

The changes are happening fast. The legal requirements are real and there is massive potential to build relevant service offerings, acquire new customers, and increase current rates of revenue and profitability growth. In addition, there's the opportunity to harness the technologies internally to deliver improvements in areas such as professional productivity, responding to client queries, proposal development, research efficiency, and completing multi-jurisdictional submissions.

There are four typical reasons for developing new practice offerings in these emergent areas. Firstly, clients ask the firm to help explore the implications of a new field it is venturing into. Indeed, many law firms now have big practices in internet law, biotech, and cloud computing because clients led them there.

A second approach is where individuals see opportunity and pursue it. A good example is US law firm Perkins Coie, where Dax Hansen, a partner in IT, payments, and international transactions, saw the opportunities arising out of digital currencies such as Bitcoin and their underlying core technology—the blockchain. Hansen launched the first legal industry blockchain practice in May 2013. The firm's blockchain practice now has over 40 lawyers focused on the legal impacts from digital currencies to capital markets and a range of distributed applications.

A third approach is becoming increasingly popular with small to medium-sized firms, where partners and relatively junior staff are seconded to spend a few days to several weeks truly immersing themselves in a client's business. This is typically done where the core technology is extremely complex, and the legal ramifications are myriad. For example, there is growing interest in the notion of cryogenically freezing someone on death (or while still alive) with the hope that one day, technology will emerge to restore the physical body, memory, and consciousness of the frozen individual.

Cryogenics has the potential to become a trillion-dollar industry within a decade, and facilities are emerging worldwide. Servicing this sector's legal needs requires a very deep understanding of cryogenics, the costs and risks involved, the customer commitments being made, the status of the science that might deliver a regeneration solution, and the current status of the sector in law.

The fourth approach is where firms acknowledge the changes taking place and decide to immerse themselves in the opportunity in the hope of building profitable legal offerings for the emerging sectors. Such firms make a conscious commitment to put professional staff at all levels through a deep immersion in the technological enablers of tomorrow's world. They run workshops and study tours to immerse their leaders and partners across the practice in a deep exploration of the technologies shaping the future and the ways in which they could transform current industries and enable new sectors. The aim is to be at the forefront in advising both the emerging sectors and those impacted by them. For example, in smart healthcare this means that firms advise the technology solution developers, hospitals, regulators, and patient groups.

The goal here is to help partners and business development professionals understand the emerging science and technology in sufficient depth to be able to start meaningful conversations with current and potential customers. Other key steps in the immersion process include joining and participating actively in the formation of industry associations, hosting events for meet-up groups in the relevant sector, attending conferences, and devoting time to reading about the client industry, and writing thought leadership articles on the legal ramifications.

For example, it is almost certain that legal considerations will not be top of mind for the 17-year-old developer of an AI facial recognition app that shows the dating history and associated comments and ratings for everyone you meet in a club. Such an app could prove very popular but fall foul of laws in a number of ways that the developer had never considered. Indeed, as we scan across AI and related technologies and the trillion-dollar sectors they are helping to spawn, the range of legal issues and resulting opportunities are almost overwhelming. For example:

- The emergence of autonomous self-driving vehicles opens up the potential for self-owning assets including buildings and public infrastructure. What issues does this raise around legal liability in the event of failure to perform or when accidents occur?
- If an AI-based system makes a poor decision that leads to a car crash, the death of a patient, or an aircraft being delayed, who will be held liable: the owners of the application, the developer of the underlying AI tool, the provider of the data set from which the system was trained, those guiding the training, or the provider of the technology platform on which the system runs?
- If AI is increasingly used for scientific discovery and the system infringes a patent, who will be held liable?

- Where AI is being used to run hugely complex and interconnected transaction platforms with the trading taking place in digital currencies and via blockchains (i.e. the source of the funds and information about the counterparties is unknown), how can the risk of fraud and money laundering be addressed?
- What procedures will be required for rollback, recovery, contract review, and dispute arbitration for fully automated AI and blockchain-based financial transaction systems?
- How should we account for the jurisdictional and taxation implications of firms that are using AI systems to move their financial assets around the world on a continuous basis in real time to attract the best second-by-second interest rates?
- How should we write the contracts for goods and services when AI tools are being used to define and combine the elements of the offering and set the pricing in real time based on the user's profile and requirements?
- Precog systems are emerging that can predict an individual's propensity to crime. What governance frameworks might be required for such AI-enabled "pre-crime" units?

We have focused quite deliberately on the potential of AI and emerging technologies to create exponential business growth opportunities in the marketplace. There are also immense opportunities to drive exponential improvements within the firm, in the products and services it provides, and in the ways it delivers its offerings. We have identified seven distinct areas of opportunity:

- Automation of legal tasks and processes;
- Decision support and outcome prediction;
- Creation of new product and service offerings;
- Development of tools and applications for in-house legal teams;
- Process design and matter management;
- Practice management; and,
- Fully automated online services.

In all of these areas, live AI applications are already in use or under development across the legal sector. In the next five years, we will see an explosion of legal opportunities arising from the transformation of existing sectors and the emergence of new ones. Artificial intelligence and related technologies will enable and accelerate the birth of new markets, commercial concepts, business models, and delivery mechanisms—spawning ideas we would struggle to get our heads around today.

Growth-motivated law firms of all sizes are "giving themselves permission" to invest the time and energy to embrace this new world thinking that could deliver exponential growth. The big question for everyone to ask is: What will it take for our firm to believe it can be a winner in the exponential future of legal?

- *What would the new quality standards for law firms be in the exponential future of legal and AI?*
- *How should law firms divide their innovation time and resources between developing new externally-focused practicing offerings and improving internal processes?*
- *What are the biggest changes we might see in the legal profession as a result of the introduction of AI?*

A version of this article was originally published in *Latin Lawyer* under the title "AI: Friend or Foe."

Blockchain, Bitcoin, and Law: A Distributed Disruption?

By Rohit Talwar and Alexandra Whittington

How can law firms take advantage of the new growth opportunities presented by developments in blockchain technology and digital currencies?

The future of the legal industry is being reshaped by a number of rapidly advancing technologies and the disruptive ideas they enable. Today's lawyers are being advised to learn to code, develop an artificial intelligence (AI) application, and outsource legal discovery tasks to machines.

One of the many new technological drivers impacting law firms is the secure information exchange/transaction ledger platform known as a blockchain. Opinions about its potential impact are divided— some see it as the basis for the reinvention of economies and global governance, while others simply see it as means of secure and incorruptible information exchange between counterparties.

This cloud-based distributed ledger technology provides a source of irrefutable record of every transaction. In legal it is enabling fully automated self-executing "smart" contracts, and has the potential to help attorneys provide new services and create new value for clients and law firms. Blockchain is known as the structure underlying Bitcoin and other digital currencies, but its applications in the legal sector are still evolving. Here we provide an overview of the technology, highlight example applications and case studies, and present a possible timeline of future developments over the next decade or so.

Overview: Blockchain and Bitcoin

Blockchain has gained notoriety lately as a potential solution to an outdated and burdensome system for managing financial transactions between counterparties. Today most financial transactions between counterparties are settled via financial intermediaries, which add time and cost to the settlement process.

Blockchain offers a distributed ledger model whereby the parties settle directly with each other, the transactions are recorded, secure, and immutable, and the counterparty identities remain anonymous. The goal is to use a "trustless" mechanism to enable a simplified and trustworthy financial ecosystem. However, in the process, these digital peer-to-peer networks also challenge the authority of institutions (banks, regulators, and governments) and are thus creating disruption.

According to its advocates, the decentralized nature of blockchain and Bitcoin will cause much-needed disruption, with reverberations far beyond the financial realm. There is an element of social revolution in blockchain, thus it is often portrayed as a conduit for challenging the status quo. Though Bitcoin, a digital currency, is an explicitly financial innovation (i.e. for payments, transfer of funds) blockchain is far less specific. Blockchain serves a critical role in the administration of Bitcoin, and there are similar platforms in place for other digital currencies.

Blockchains can also be used to complete a range of other tasks, and track the movement, transfer, and ownership of all sorts of things besides money. Example applications include luxury goods, education credits, property titles, and patents, to name a few. Blockchain is structured like a traditional accounting tool: at its core is a ledger that tracks deposits in and payments out and maintains a running balance. However, its uses go far beyond counting coins.

Lest we assume blockchain and Bitcoin are solely the tools of the far-left, libertarians, anarchists, and socialists among us, this technology has captured the attention of global business and industry to the tune of millions of dollars. Among banks alone, one source projects spending on blockchain solutions to grow from over US$200 million in 2017, and US$300 million in 2018, to US$400 million in 2019.[5] Perhaps ironically, a great wave of enthusiasm for blockchain now emanates from the business establishment, including stalwarts like banking, finance, real estate, and law.

Bitcoin is by far the leading digital currency at present. At the time of writing, its valuation had reached US$18,000—giving it a market capitalization of around US$305 billion. The issue here is that few would use their precious coins to buy goods and services if they expected the value of the coin—and hence the effective cost of the purchase—to increase by 50% within a few weeks.

Applications to Law Firms

While the basic metaphor for blockchain is an automated checkbook register that instantly reconciles transactions, there are several other concepts inherent to blockchain, which are ideally suited for applications in law firms. Current legal industry activity around blockchain ranges from the simple—payment for services rendered, verification of contracts, representing companies conducting business on the blockchain—through to the highly complex, such as formulation of an entirely new legal system altogether.

Clearly, a supranational legal system would usurp local or national laws to create a globally agreed upon set of codes that govern rights during a dispute. Examples like this demonstrate the potential scale of blockchain's legal sector applications. In terms of contracts and payments, though, the firms now adopting blockchain are attracted to its practicality: It reduces the resources needed to complete day-to-day operations. For example, Goldman Sachs estimates that $US11 to $US12 billion per year could be saved with blockchain-based clearing and settlement of cash securities, with $US2 to $US4 billion yearly savings from moving real estate titles to distributed ledgers.[6]

A growing number of industry examples demonstrate the diversity of applications of blockchain and Bitcoin to legal services:

- International law firm Steptoe & Johnson helps clients in all industries manage application of the Blockchain in their businesses, and accepts Bitcoin as payment for fees.[7]
- King & Wood Mallesons (headquartered in Hong Kong) has several dozen lawyers who have a focus on blockchain, including smart contracts.[8]
- Perkins Coie LLP partner Dax Hansen (US) launched the first blockchain legal industry practice in 2013, which has grown to over 40 lawyers focused on blockchain technology, digital currencies, and distributed applications of all types.[9]
- Selachii (UK) is implementing self-executing smart contracts on blockchain, starting with wills, title registries, and shareholder agreements.[10]
- Allens (Australia) wrote a report suggesting that the future of the legal business model, which profits from an absence of trust between organizations, is imperiled by the rise of blockchain technology.[11]

Outside of law firms themselves, the start-up ecosystem has many examples of services geared toward marrying procedural business practices with blockchain:

- Juro uses blockchain technology on the Ethereum network to underpin the creation and signing of legal contracts.[12]
- The Decentralized Arbitration and Mediation Network (DAMN) operates as a network of smart contracts on the Ethereum blockchain, creating an "opt-in justice system for commercial transactions" as a new form of cross-border dispute resolution.[13]
- CommonAccord is creating global codes of legal transactions, automating legal documents such as master service agreements.[14]
- DAO.LINK is an initiative which facilitates brick-and-mortar business interactions with blockchain-based organizations.[15]

Timeline of Possible Future Blockchain Developments in Law

Based on the pace of developments to date, we see the following as a plausible expansion of the role of blockchain in the legal sector:

Next 18 months: ETA 2018-2019

- Growing use of smart contracts.
- Increasing acceptance of digital currencies as payment for legal services.
- Proliferation of consortiums to integrate blockchain into business practices across different sectors.
- Several blockchain start-ups acquired by large banks, law firms, and consulting firms.
- At least half of the top 200 global law firms working with clients interested in engaging in blockchain transactions.
- A number of case examples of asset owners fighting counterfeits and patent violations with blockchain.
- Multiple instances of real estate transactions, deeds, and new financial instruments being recorded on blockchains.

Next 3 years: ETA 2020-2021

- A proliferation of blockchain-based distributed autonomous organizations (DAOs) with no workers and no bosses, just algorithms.
- Numerous examples of merger and acquisition transactions conducted on "auto pilot" using blockchain and AI.
- Elimination of some jobs and roles (banker, advisor, lawyer).
- Merging of AI and blockchain; robolawyers on blockchain.

Next 5 years: ETA 2023-2028

- Deployment of a DAMN – a global supranational legal system for international dispute resolution.
- Automation of arbitration, dispute resolution, and various legal and banking processes—eliminating more roles in law firms and banks.

- Creation of new professional roles to deal with the legal ramifications of the spread of blockchain.

5-10 years: ETA 2028-2033

- The rise of Algocracy: Law is code, code is law.
- The first distributed autonomous societies (DAS) with automation of services, justice, rights, and laws.

Blockchain and cryptocurrency gained unprecedented ground in 2017. The central bank of China is piloting a blockchain-based cryptocurrency, possibly a very loud signal about the rising status of the technology which will legitimize its use.[16] Another indicator comes in the form of headlines screaming about Bitcoin's price trends, earning investors millions and suggesting that cryptocurrencies are now firmly in the public consciousness.

As futurists, we expect that for every big wave of change, there are dozens or hundreds of small ripples; the revolutionary nature of Bitcoin and blockchain means it will disrupt businesses of all kinds. Because it involves money, contracts, and ownership, this is a special consideration for lawyers and their firms.

Starting now, law firms owe it to their staffs and teams to begin a conversation about blockchain, Bitcoin, and other digital currencies. Information, in this case, is power—blockchain's distributed disruption of banks, laws, and most traditional social institutions will generate new conflicts, anxieties, and tensions for which a legal remedy may be the only solution. It is a likely topic of future legal matters.

Keep in mind that the best way of describing blockchain is "distributed," in other words, absent of central authority. A lot of the projects in the works seek to apply this thinking to society at large through DAS', DAOs, and distributed legal systems. If a distributed mindset prevails, this will be of direct relevance to lawyers, judges, law enforcement, and anyone in occupations that rely on a centralized legal system.

Furthermore, the entire basic model of business conduct stands to be disrupted on the same scale as it was during the rise of the internet as a business tool. Blockchain, in combination with other technologies like artificial intelligence and cloud computing, is likely to lead to the transformation of the very basis of business, productivity, and possibly even money itself. By decentralizing the powers that be, blockchain seems set to be a high-tech disruption that will challenge law at every level and function.

- *How might the legal sector react to the decentralization of power in society as a result of blockchain applications?*
- *What could be the role of law firms in a future where laws are coded?*
- *How might law firms capitalize on new opportunities and business models enabled by AI, blockchain, and cloud computing?*

A version of this article was originally published in *Legal Solutions by Thomson Reuters* under the title "Blockchain, Bitcoin, and Law: A Distributed Disruption."

Educating the City of the Future: A Lifewide Learning Experience

By Rohit Talwar, Steve Wells, April Koury, Alexandra Whittington, and Maria Romero

How might smart cities strategies impact the future of education for citizens?

Cities worldwide are competing to build highly interconnected "smart city" environments. The aim is for people, government, civil society, the education sector, and business to operate in symbiosis with powerful exponentially improving technologies. These include big data, the Internet of things (IoT), cloud computing, artificial intelligence (AI), autonomous vehicles, 3D/4D printing, and renewable energy.

Smart cities hold the promise of a high quality of life by design. At the same time, the smart city mindset emphasizes and relies on the potentially contentious pervasive surveillance and data capture of all residents. However, to make informed choices, citizens need sufficient digital literacy to understand what is being done and the implications of being under near-total surveillance. So, if the pursuit of "smart" becomes a key driver in the evolving future of cities as communities and economic centers, how might this affect education and adult learning? Here we explore the potential impact of smart city planning on education and human development.

Learn Anywhere, Anytime

One of the first priorities is to ensure that all of the key players truly understand the new technologies and what they enable. For example, a critical and constant infrastructure planning challenge is how big to build a school, hospital, or other public service building for the future? The lead time from design, planning, and construction through to occupancy can be significant.

So firstly, AI could help in the planning phase by analyzing demographics and local economic trends. The analysis could also factor in key infrastructure construction project data, outcomes for similar projects around the world, and the implications for service delivery. Secondly, emerging construction techniques such as modular construction, 3D printing, self-healing materials, embedded sensors, and new data storage technologies could help build flexibility into new buildings. In both cases, the planners, architects, engineers, and construction partners involved need to ensure they are abreast of the true capabilities of these new technology tools.

From an instructional delivery perspective, AI could augment reality around the smart city with educational experiences which inspire learning. Personal AI would be able to create tailored learning opportunities anytime, anyplace. However, to get the most from portable education technology, physical spaces need to be interactive and flexible. Smart cities could achieve this with a blanket of sensors embedded in the infrastructure that could provide accurate information about public space usage.

Multi-surface, experiential, and outdoors learning would be encouraged in a smart city. With real-time data, local governments and citizens could decide how to use the resources available more efficiently. So, for example, schooling and classrooms could be decoupled from fixed buildings, with the learning experiences tasking place at a range of different geographical locations within the same neighborhood. This might reduce the amount of physical space required for a school, as a proportion of the pupils would always be out on location.

When Student Engagement is Civic Engagement

An AI backbone supporting smart city life should allow for deep personalization and contextualization of learning. For example, an engineering student could utilize smart technologies to learn about mega skyscraper construction within the context of the smart city in which she lives. The AI could take into account the details of the locality of the project, build in relevant local and cultural considerations, and even incorporate information about the methodologies and experience of the various partners on the project. This type of student engagement would raise local involvement and potentially increase civic engagement—a win-win.

Smart cities should be inherently sustainable because of intricate provisioning and monitoring of public resources, such as roadways and energy. With a built-in focus on guarding the commons, students in a smart city would ideally and naturally obtain a sense of the value of balance and responsibility for the public good. Through strategies involving rewards (and possibly punishments), smart cities could enforce policies that support the smooth flow of traffic, avoid waste, and maximize energy use, among other benefits.

The ability to create behavioral change will be both a risk and a benefit to education in a smart city context, treading the fine line between surveillance and privacy. When it comes to young children in particular, there may be special considerations for buildings that record one's every move, prompt activities that might violate free will, and use facial recognition monitoring. Schools will be key settings in which to define the socially accepted boundaries of observational technology.

Teaching Smarter

Even when technology has the power to make the everyday activities within smart cities more predictable, there will be no such thing as a "normal day," especially regarding education. While AI might teach the more technical lessons, teachers could gravitate towards a life coach role that inspires those in their charge. One-on-one conversations would create closer relationships between mentors and mentees.

Credits may be awarded for developing socialization skills through interactions with diverse audiences online and in the local community—becoming another data point that smart cities could track. Rather than grades, or perhaps as a supplement to grades, students might be assessed by their community credits and socialization scores.

Businesses could be involved in the training and education of the future workforce and could also play a part in developing new curricula. Artificial intelligence would be the enabling technology for schools to provide an education curriculum that evolves with the expected future needs of the business world. The World Economic Forum predicts that two thirds of today's primary school children will work in job types that don't yet exist, implying that a world comprised of smart cities needs to create learning experiences fit for the future of work rather than the past or present.[17]

Conclusion

A well-thought-out smart city vision, enabled by a robust and well-executed plan, could provide the foundation stones for the next stage of social development. This implies a world where science and technology are genuinely harnessed in service of creating a very human future. Clearly the role of education in molding well-educated, conscientious citizens is central to the realization of this vision of the future.

- *How might the private and public sector integrate their efforts and resources in order to create a very human community?*
- *How can we prepare future generations of individuals and businesses for the level of data capture and potential invasions of privacy required in the cities of the future?*
- *How can we ensure that a new technology enabled education system will unleash humans' potential talents?*

A version of the article was originally published in *Independent Education Today* under the title "Educating the City of the Future: A Lifewide Learning Experience."

Food Production in a Hyper-Tech Future: Robochefs, VR Taste Tests, and Lab-Grown Meat?

By Rohit Talwar, Steve Wells, April Koury, Karolina Dolatowska, Maria Romero, and Alexandra Whittington

How might technological innovations impact the food ecosystem, and what new business models and opportunities may arise?

So, it's official: Burger- and bratwurst-flipping robots became a thing in 2017—the robots have most definitely arrived in the kitchen. However, there is much more to come in the years ahead when we think about the potential applications of artificial intelligence (AI) and other cutting-edge technologies to the future of food production.

Developments in 3D printing, cloud computing, big data, block-chain, and the Internet of things (IoT) will introduce new possibilities to the industry. These diverse technologies will be bound together by AI, providing powerful insights to help change every facet of food production, distribution, and retailing. What transformations for food and beverage production could occur in the aftermath of various bursts of innovation rising from these new technologies with seemingly magical powers?

Thinking ahead to 2025, distinct images of the future start to come into view. For example, could celebrity-inspired robochefs custom-make personalized meals based on a cloud-stored digital profile which takes into account each diner's personal preferences, dietary issues, allergies, and health records? As a form of food manufacturing, personalized food could be achieved with 3D printing, with the factory providing the ingredients. The food would then be printed in the consumer's home or a local food fabrication center, which could be anything from a school kitchen to your local cafe.

Such approaches to future food production would create opportunities for manufacturers to interact with consumers more directly, perhaps using blockchain to eliminate the information loss that normally occurs through layers of middlemen like transport and retail.

Decentralized food and beverage manufacturing might even offer automated ordering via the devices in your home connected via the IoT. So called smart contracts would automate payments, and our cloud-based "digital twins" would do the ordering. The key here is to convey and regularly update the supplier with consumers' tastes and preferences via the constant monitoring of their behavior 24/7 by the technology. Such advances suggest the food production supply chain could be completely transformed.

Rising future food demands could in part be met by urban vertical gardens, self-driving trucks, and autonomous food transport drones, extending the manufacturers' reach in previously unimaginable ways. Virtual reality and augmented reality also offer unconventional access to consumers from the manufacturing side—simulated taste, smell, and even touch may soon become part of selling a food and drink experience.

The ability to test new ideas and access new markets in mixed reality is a huge new opportunity for food and drink manufacturers. Picture the scene: The consumer creates their ideal meal, including taste, smell, touch, and visual presentation. The food is then robo-picked from the manufacturer's town center based vertical farm, the meal is prepared by the robo-chef in the back of the autonomous delivery vehicle, and then transported and flash heated by a drone that literally places the meal on your dining table. Every technological element of this scenario currently exists, or will exist within a year or two at the outside.

Other reality-bending ideas, such as laboratory-grown meats and the incorporation of insect-based protein, are potentially paradigm-shifting transformations that are gathering pace and could potentially shock the food industry. The price of laboratory grown hamburgers has fallen from €325,000 per patty to just €11 in only three years and could reach 10 to 50 cents by the end of the decade.

The prospect of farmlands auto-worked with zero human intervention is another shift that could have a dramatic impact: Imagine the agricultural industry with no waste, high efficiency, no labor abuses, and high resource management. Creating sustainable abundance should take top priority when it comes to integrating new technologies into the food production vision of the future.

- *How might technological innovations help increase the social aspect of eating?*
- *How could the food industry address concerns around synthetic or artificially altered foods?*
- *How far would we want automation to penetrate our leisure dining experiences—would we pay more or less for a meal prepared by a robo-chef with two Michelin stars than by its human counterpart?*

A version of this article was originally published in *Food & Beverage Magazine* under the title "Food Production in a Hyper-Tech Future: Robochefs, VR Taste Tests, and Lab-Grown Meat?"

REIMAGINING BUSINESS

Businesses and Technology – Time for a Code of Ethics?

By Rohit Talwar and Katharine Barnett

How can businesses ensure an ethical approach to the use of increasingly disruptive and invasive technologies?

Rapid digital technological advances are penetrating every sector and forcing firms of all sizes to think about the potentially far-reaching implications of these powerful new tools on jobs, privacy, security, and the way we communicate. A failure on any or all of these fronts could damage the brand and its "license to trade." This realization is driving many to develop codes of ethics specifically in relation to the uses of these new technologies.

General codes of businesses ethics are becoming more commonplace and are often encouraged by trade bodies. However, there is less widespread adoption of analogous codes of digital ethics. Business leaders, CEOs, and heads of departments are in pivotal positions to guide the formation, implementation, and compliance with such codes. This chapter highlights upcoming areas of potential concern and strategies that business leaders can adopt in forming digital ethics codes.

The use of powerful technologies is increasing in firms of every size as prices fall and access becomes easier, particularly in using online Software as a Service (SaaS) solutions. These can make high functionality software applications and services available to even the smallest of firms for a relatively affordable monthly fee, thus enabling them to compete with larger and better-resourced players.

Many are exploiting the transformative potential of technologies such as artificial intelligence (AI), cloud storage, big data, the Internet of things (IoT), wearable devices, and blockchain. The goals are typically to enable new offerings, enhance service, maximize efficiency, cut costs, and improve marketing and sales effectiveness.

These technologies raise new ethical issues; notions of privacy and ownership are being challenged; and questions arise over who owns customer data and how it can be used: What license do we have to aggregate, analyze, and interpret information gleaned from hundreds, thousands, or millions of customer interactions?

Informed consent processes are becoming necessary and ideas on what constitutes harm and fair use are being called into question. These challenges are arising across industry value chains, so no one is surprised to see businesses develop digital codes to ensure employees, clients, and partners know they are operating within acceptable ethical standards. Those in organizational and functional leadership roles are in key positions to instigate and steer the ethical discourse to enable each company to form its code.

Technological Upheaval

There are many potential ethical questions being raised around new technologies. The ubiquity of the IoT may raise concerns about the extent to which employee behavior can be monitored; for example, is the amount of food staff consumed by individuals something the company could or should monitor? Should companies aggregate and analyze data from employees' wearable health trackers? Is such wellness monitoring beneficial or invasive? Brain scanning technology is already in place to monitor employee concentration—is this appropriate or invasive?

As stress levels in the workplace rise, is tracking health and mental activity a natural extension of monitoring productivity? Powerful technologies are no longer simply mechanical tools; they are increasingly redefining the nature and scope of employees' work and their relationship with the employer. Hence it is critical for those in leadership to set the tone around the use of technology and data. What is commercially sensible may seem ethically questionable, challenging the boundaries of privacy and sensitivity. Just because we can, does it mean we should?

Public Dialogue

With an accelerating pace of digital disruption across society, critical ethical questions are moving up the public agenda faster. For example, in the last two years we have seen intense public debate around fair presentation of information on social media, the rise of the "post truth" society, and the employment implications of AI. Corporations cannot sit on the sidelines in these discussions. In some sense, there is no template to follow; there is no gold standard or global consensus over what is considered ethical. Businesses must engage in continual public and professional dialogue to determine what is permissible, what is acceptable, and what would be best for shareholders, employees, and customers.

Regular discourse highlights emerging issues and potential solutions. For example, if unbridled monitoring of employees' health trackers is generally considered invasive, informed consent systems can be adopted with transparent monitoring options defined for employees to select from. Choices can be agreed with staff on the extent of monitoring, with clearly established employee opt out clauses.

As business leaders, we must stay abreast of technological progress and engage with the questions being raised by the technologies, other organizations' choices, and societal responses. This engagement can help inform choice, providing alternative scenarios and ideas that drive our own ethical guidelines.

Compliance and Consistency

A clear internal view of what is considered ethically permissible is vital for any organization. Once ethical frameworks have been established, for them to be taken seriously, these guiding principles must become cornerstones of strategic policy with regular monitoring of adherence. The organization must be seen to be running its decisions through these frameworks and rejecting or adapting plans that would be in breach of the code.

To be effective, the guiding principles must underpin subsequent actions consistently. Conformance with digital ethical cannot be a gray area or easily bypassed because of commercial considerations. Alongside driving home the message in regular communications and public statements, leaders need to demonstrate case examples of clear choices that have been made or rejected because of digital ethics. Corrective measures must be clear and applied consistently when these guidelines are bypassed.

Leading the Way

The necessity to form codes of digital ethics will increase, and the next three to five years could see widespread adoption—with some firms losing out where they don't meet customers' ethical expectations. In a world where the public discourse is almost impossible to control, CEOs must lead the way in ensuring their firms adopt and hold themselves to the highest standards of digital ethical behavior and respond accordingly when gaps in the framework emerge. As the world becomes increasingly digital and it becomes harder to distinguish our offerings from those of our competitors, who we are and what we stand for will become critical differentiators.

- *How should businesses assess the trade-offs between business value and individual privacy around their use of employee and customer data?*
- *What role could exemplar businesses be playing in the public dialogue on data privacy and security?*
- *What are the critical behaviors required of executives and managers if they are to serve as ethical role models in the use of digital practices?*

A version of this article was originally published in *Business Review Europe* under the title "Why businesses need a code of ethics for use of technology."

Staying Relevant – Five Fundamentals of Leading the Future for HR and Training

By Rohit Talwar, Steve Wells, Alexandra Whittington, and Maria Romero

How might the role and value of HR and training evolve in the rapidly evolving future of business?

Technology and its many uses promise to reshape society and business in dramatic ways in the decade ahead. The arrival of the Fourth Industrial Revolution—characterized by smart machines—will force a fundamental rethinking of the nature of firms and markets, organizational roles and designs, and people's place and value within them. Whether we pursue the path of using technology to eliminate the workforce, or to truly unleash human potential, HR and training should be central to the business transformation process. The rapidly changing reality of business will undoubtedly create new opportunities, sweet spots, and stress points for HR and training.

Should we wait for disruption and future shocks before we respond? Alternatively, are there practical steps we can take now to prepare for a range of possible outcomes and thereby increase our resilience in the face of uncertainty? Here we explore actionable ideas to help HR and training prepare for the inevitable surprises that these changes might bring.

Tomorrow's world of work will be shaped in large part by artificial intelligence (AI) combined with successive waves of exponentially improving, transformational science and technology developments such as blockchain, big data, hyperconnectivity, cloud computing, the Internet of everything, 3D/4D printing, synthetic biology, new materials, and human brain and body enhancements.

These developments could make the typical user experience of office technology far more interactive than ever before, with smart technologies that seem to respond and evolve based on users' needs and wants. Soon, the workplace might be populated by humans, robots, digital entities (i.e. algorithms), and hybrid augmented human workers performing side by side, each with a say in how things get done.

In the face of such potentially seismic changes, the first step is for business leadership and the HR and training functions to decide on the future role they should be playing in helping the organization prepare for and navigate potentially transformational change. For example, there is an emerging spectrum of possible roles for HR, from administering people procedures through to ensuring the organization has awareness of and access to all the resources required to secure future business success.

In the future, an evolved "resourcing function" might have a remit that ranges from capability and workforce planning to internal staffing, and procuring external partners, services, technologies, research, and advice. Hence the Chief Resourcing Officer might work in tandem with the Chief Operating Officer to guarantee the latter has access to all the elements required to transform and run the business.

A key driver for HR's evolution is that the potential future applications and impacts of AI and its sister technologies are almost limitless and unknowable. We are too early in its evolution to know how far AI could replicate and ultimately exceed the human brain's capabilities. Predicting the reactions of humans, businesses, governments, and civil society is almost impossible as there is limited understanding across society today of AI's true potential. There is seemingly even less willingness to think deeply about the possible impacts and consequences. Hence HR has the opportunity to step into the vacuum to start anticipating and preparing for inevitable surprises.

Forecasts vary of how many jobs could be replaced or created by technological disruption. Whether 80% of jobs are eliminated or 50% more created, the new jobs will require advanced skillsets and different mindsets. The transition will be dramatic, painful, and require new knowledge and competences. Governments, businesses, and civil society will need to rethink the assumptions and mechanisms that underpin our world. Human resources and training could become central to helping envision different possible futures and helping organizations get there.

Already, in business, fundamental changes are taking place in the way organizations are using technology. Many are embarking on radical digital overhauls, enabling them to deliver new offerings, enhance service, improve efficiency, and increase cost competitiveness.

The emerging technologies of the corporate ecosystem will have economic, social, and environmental implications that change the workforce, work models, and people development. Digital transformation is likely to spread throughout the business world, and wide-scale automation will inevitably lead to job reductions across economic sectors—from mining and manufacturing, to transport, retail, and finance.

In parallel, new sectors are emerging and creating opportunities. Under favorable conditions, the global economy could grow from about US$75 trillion in 2017 to around US$120 trillion over the next decade—over half of this could come from industries and businesses that are just emerging or don't yet exist. No one yet knows if these newcomers will generate enough jobs to replace those displaced by technology.

While there might be a temptation and tendency to wait and see because the challenges seem so immense, this could be calamitously risky. The changes will cascade and accelerate rapidly, overwhelming and paralyzing unprepared governments, businesses, societies, and individuals.

Strategically, it seems far more prudent to prepare for a range of possible scenarios and to try to anticipate impending shocks and risks. The insights can help us to act now to start putting society and business on a more sustainable footing, thus ensuring sufficient resilience to cope with the risk of large-scale technological unemployment. Here we identify five fundamental actions that forward-looking organizations, governments, societies, and individuals should be thinking about right now. These factors could occupy an increasing amount of the workload for HR and training.

1. Rethinking Education at Every Level

Success in the future will require a smart, adaptable, and highly educated workforce. Indeed, many commentators and some governments anticipate that within a decade, most new jobs will require graduate level education at a minimum. How those qualifications are acquired may well look very different to today.

To survive and thrive in business, there is a need to understand both the technologies and the mindsets shaping the future. Mindset is key here—there are plenty of technological competitors to Uber and Airbnb—for the latter, their true point of difference is their mindset, a radically different way of thinking about how to deliver on customer desires without owning any assets or employing any service delivery staff.

Job one for HR and training must be raising technological literacy. We must ensure that, throughout the organization, leaders, managers, and employees truly understand these future-shaping technologies, how they might impact different sectors, and the new ways of thinking, business models, and delivery approaches they are enabling. Much of the required content is already available through free online platforms—the key is building it into the training and development agenda.

People will also need support developing higher-level skills that will help them learn rapidly and transition into jobs that don't even exist today. These skills may include collaboration, problem solving, navigating complexity, scenario thinking, and accelerated learning. Clearly, businesses can play a major role here in helping their own staff transition to new roles in the organization or new jobs elsewhere.

More broadly, we also believe a massive increase is required in the provision of free adult education across society. This could be done using existing facilities in businesses, schools, and higher education institutions. Most teaching and meeting spaces in these facilities are unused in the evenings; why not put them to use for continuing adult education? Some of the teachers and lecturers would ideally come from the emerging growth sectors of the future—helping students understand their context and mindset.

Pupil-teacher ratios at school level will also need to be reduced to increase personalized support–the evidence is clear on the impact. This also means re-evaluating the expectations for students pursuing higher education: A well-educated workforce is needed to propel the country forward, and while many other nations provide free degree level education, some still need to develop a sustainable solution that doesn't leave future generations demotivated, disillusioned, and saddled with debts that many cannot repay. Employers can play a big role here in lobbying government to think strategically about the financing of higher education.

Education and work have shaped the way society functions. Redefining both of these fundamental institutions will generate a series of opportunities for HR including:

- Compulsory participation in technology awareness programs for those seeking promotion.
- Providing immersions on critical technologies and their possible impacts.
- Developing life-long and life-wide learning paths to support employee education beyond the organization itself, and growing such programs to include workplace coaching and training in diverse life skills and knowledge such as accelerated learning, problem solving, career path planning, and collaboration.

- Embracing such life-wide learning programs might incorporate the accrual of education microcredits or nano-credits, which would be similar to video game badges. Sensors and self-quantification would certify achievements in and out of the classrooms, so the nano-credit system could become completely automated.
- Developing closer workplace-school relationships, e.g. workplace experts instructing vocational classes at schools, students visiting workplaces regularly, providing physical community learning spaces, and involving corporate HR teams in the development of schools' curricula.

2. Experimenting with Guaranteed Basic Incomes and Services

Firms pursuing high levels of automation will need customers to buy their goods and services; however, widespread automation could dramatically reduce employment and societal purchasing power. Hence, many in Silicon Valley in particular argue for some form of automation tax to fund the provision of unconditional basic incomes (UBI) and services (UBS) across society. Some governments reject the idea on ideological grounds because they think it reeks of socialism or communism.

A number of governments also recognize that something needs to be done to avoid large-scale social decline and potential citizen unrest. Countries including Finland, Germany, and Canada have undertaken UBI experiments to understand the concept, test out different options, assess the social impact, measure the costs, and prepare themselves while they still have time. For HR, this could mean:

- Taking the lead role in modeling alternative future workforce strategies.
- Educating the workforce on the importance of taking control of their own earning capacity.
- Assessing the potential business impact of automation taxes based on different workforce scenarios.

- Providing support to help displaced workers access new skills and jobs.
- Lobbying governments to conduct early pilots of alternate UBI/UBS models to avoid being caught flat-footed as and when technological unemployment starts increasing.

3. A Massive Expansion of Support for Start-Up Creation

While the jobs outlook is uncertain, the only thing we can assume for certain is that people will need to take more responsibility for their incomes. Many will do this through the creation of small and micro-businesses that are far more immune to the risks of technology replacing humans. Employers can play a massive role here in providing start-up training and mentoring through the early phases of business creation for employees they are replacing with technology.

The most forward thinking businesses might even co-invest with such start-ups to help them get going and potentially provide them a route to market. A massive expansion of support for start-up creation would both generate jobs for the mentors and accelerate the rate at which people can build new businesses and create new jobs. In addition, HR could:

- Provide access to simple online platforms for business creation, marketing, networking, financial management, invoicing, accounting, and tax submission, enabling founders to focus on the development of their business.
- Encourage and support staff to spin out innovation initiatives from within the firm as separate businesses, possibly with financial support.
- Provide an incubator space and mentoring support for employees to work up new ideas in their spare time prior to starting out on their own.
- Create regular showcases to enable past employees to present their business offerings to potential customers.
- Commit to buying a certain amount of goods and services from firms run or managed by past employees.

- Provide a panel of executives who could act as ongoing advisors to start-ups for their first few years in business.
- Provide crowdsourcing platforms where past employees could trade ideas, requirements, and opportunities with each other.
- Provide new ventures with a blockchain based smart contract service so that contract creation and execution can be fully automated against standard rules.

4. Research and Development in Key Knowledge Sectors

A competitive economy demands cutting edge innovation. Not all R&D lends itself to assessment based on the return on investment—some just has to be undertaken for the betterment of society. Hence, expanding research funding and the number of research institutions are important enablers of tomorrow's job creation. While the firm's core R&D agenda might be driven by other functions, HR could play a key role in ensuring governments understand the knowledge base and skills sets required to feed to future of business.

The pace of change within organizations also opens up a role for HR and training to lead research into the capabilities required to run and grow tomorrow's enterprise. These might include:

- How best to educate and train leaders, managers, and employees on critical technologies and their applications within the business.
- How best to manage and mentor in environments populated by humans, robots, AI, and augmented individuals.
- Researching the possible future evolution of their core business and adjacent sectors to identify the skills that might fuel the industry.
- Exploring what other new knowledge pools need to be developed to serve the future needs of the business.
- Helping the organization to master the skills required by the leadership of the future, such as foresight, collaboration, empathy, soft skills, and comfort with complexity and uncertainty.

5. Addressing the Mental Health Challenge

Across society, the scale and severity of mental health issues are rising, a trend that large-scale job displacement is likely to increase. An enlightened, combined approach for government and business would be to fund people to train as therapists while still working today. This would ensure that they will be ready to help when the challenge becomes a major problem in a few years' time. For HR, there are clear priorities here:

- Increasing the provision of mental health support in the workplace, especially in the run up to and during massive layoffs.
- Reinforcing the importance of mentally healthy employees and discouraging the workaholic culture.
- Providing multigenerational therapy to cope with conflicts that emerge from divergent generational worldviews in the workplace.
- Encouraging employees to develop interests and personal identities beyond their occupation.
- Supporting cultural and behavioral change in areas of the organization where the management style and operating culture increase workplace stress.

Preparing for the Next Future

There's clearly a cost associated with enabling all of the five activities, but the question must be raised: What might the risks and potential costs of inaction be? A short-term focus on cost control could lead to a very long-term increase in the cost of funding unemployment benefits and policing a society that feels let down.

The future could be a very exciting place where society can tackle current challenges and create new opportunities. New industry sectors such as laboratory grown food, vertical farming, autonomous vehicles, clean water technologies, renewable energy, and synthetic materials all hold great possibilities for humanity. However, these businesses will be highly automated from the outset, and will require very different capabilities and a highly skilled workforce. The transition to these new roles will not be smooth but, as Albert Einstein once said, "In the middle of difficulty lies opportunity." For HR and training, there is tremendous potential here to play an enhanced strategic and operational role in ensuring a very human future.

- *How might we start the conversation about HR and training playing an enhanced strategic role in the organization?*
- *What might be the strategic and operational priorities for a new organizational resourcing function?*
- *What capabilities might be required to lead and manage diverse work teams composed of humans, augmented humans, AI, and robots?*

A version of the article was originally published in *Training Journal* under the title "Staying Relevant – Five Fundamentals of Leading the Future for HR and Training."

A Tomorrow Fit for Humans – Ten Priorities for the HR Director

By Rohit Talwar and Alexandra Whittington

How might technological advances impact how work gets done and the way we use our best resources to do it?

Though it has the word "human" in the title, don't expect HR to remain immune to the impacts of automation, robotics, and artificial intelligence (AI). Technology is reshaping every aspect of society, and its potential HR implications are vast and still revealing themselves. Hiring, training, and recordkeeping are just some of the areas where technology is set to impact the work of the HR function.

The HR mandate of the future is not completely predictable, but there are some solid indications of the direction things are heading. For HR, there are four key domains of impact:

- The role of emerging technologies in transforming the business and helping the workforce adapt;
- New ways of organizing people, working, and learning are being enabled by technology;
- Organizations are being challenged to address the broader societal impacts of business choices such as technological unemployment; and,
- New technologies could transform the purpose, work, and impact of the HR function itself in a number of ways.

Below, we explore ten key areas of potential impact of technological advances within the organization and in HR that HR directors and leaders need to have on their radars.

1. Rethinking Workspace – The Rise of Smart Cities and Buildings

As much of our environment becomes "smart," this enables entirely different approaches to workforce and workspace management. The smart city provides a digital infrastructure, so traffic, policing, public transportation, and crowd movement can be monitored and managed by a central authority in the interest of maximum efficiency and safety. In terms of preventing congestion around car accidents, for example, a stretch of road prone to accidents during rush hour could be patrolled, or have cars rerouted from the area. Such decisions are made based on an analysis of big data drawn from a range of sensors constantly monitoring their environment.

The same concept is likely to be applied to smart buildings and their workforce occupants; elevator lines could be coordinated, or shift work scheduled and adjusted instantaneously, based on patterns of activity and behavior reflected in the data. For HR, this could mean documentation of workplace incidents could become the domain of the surveillance systems embedded in smart buildings. Would this bring an end to the investigation of workplace disputes? If firms become part of the interconnected smart city, would they be required to feed in employee data? If so, then privacy, behavior modification, data profiling, and surveillance are potential hot button issues that HR must handle.

2. Continuous Organization Redesign – Adapting to AI

We are witnessing the rise of artificial intelligence (AI), and with it comes notions such as the AI lawyer, accountant, doctor, and stockbroker. The next few years will see AI and other disruptive technologies become embedded across business functions and management activities. Organizations must be prepared to respond to the likely speed of change and the exponential improvements that become possible in product development, service delivery, and customer service.

It's too soon to predict how AI managers will conduct business, but they may well increase the pace and efficiency with which the organization functions. In response, firms are moving into a state of near continuous redesign. Hence HR needs to think about how to ensure a rapid and effective response to rapidly changing personnel and training requirements. An AI in the C-suite isn't far off, but how it might play out is hugely uncertain.

3. Blended and Swarm Workforces – Gig Workers of the World, Unite

It is now common for firms to use a blend of internal and contract talent and adopt the swarm model. The aim is to pull together quickly the teams of employees, partner companies, and "gig worker" contractors required to deliver projects—much like the way a film crew assembles and disbands when the movie is completed.

Gig work has its opponents, but others see it as being great for those wanting to work flexible hours and amass a portfolio of non-routine experiences. A key role for HR here is to help with forming and disbanding such teams as smoothly and rapidly as possible, and sharing best practices from across the organizations and externally to keep refining the swarm approach.

Lately freelancers have expressed a need to convene and interact. A global gig worker collective called Enspiral, for instance, involves a combination of face-to-face meeting rooms, open-source technology, and digital organizing as the foundation of a form of social safety net for freelance workers. Members can share ideas, meals, contacts, and projects.

As the 9-to-5 job becomes extinct, the rise of freelancing is revealing some increasingly unmet needs—social, emotional, and intellectual, to name a few—that were once fulfilled in the workplace. HR professionals could play a valuable role in helping to organize gig economy workers around the common goals and interests they share.

4. Team Focus, Rewards, and Tools – HR by Algorithm

In the digital age, there is growing discussion about how to design teams and how to manage a workforce that might include humans, robots, and smart software, with each playing a key role. While we know the new technologies on the horizon can save time, money, and resources, we don't yet know their limitations, and there are still areas where humans are more effective.

Google's two-year study, Project Aristotle, revealed that despite the tremendous caliber of data analysts and data engineers, relying on data analysis alone was inadequate to provide a formula for team-building success.[18] No algorithm could form better work teams—it requires a human touch to select the best, most effective groups. As we become more technology-dependent and the geeks inherit the Earth, HR must ensure these new masters of the universe have the emotional intelligence and interpersonal skills to communicate with each other and the businesses they serve.

5. Talent Wars/The Alliance – Tours of Duty/ Outsourcing HR

New patterns of engagement are required to motivate and retain talent. The idea of "tours of duty" in different projects and areas of the business will become more common. The ability to outsource almost any job, including HR, will also transform workplaces. For example, two leading Chinese start-ups, UR Work and Woo Space, don't just offer workspace for short-term and sporadic use; they also provide a network for to exchange services such as HR for small companies and start-ups. As space-sharing morphs into new partnerships and opportunities, and technologies make it simpler to handle a fluctuating workforce, HR may require more flexibility.

6. Short Interval Scheduling – Managing Attention Deficit

Firms are finding that the new generations coming into the workforce want freedom and responsibility, but may lack the skills to navigate and prioritize open-ended work tasks. Hence there's a growing interest in the use of short interval scheduling to break larger tasks into more manageable daily or even hourly deliverables. This also allows for more regular feedback to a generation that has grown used to constant affirmation through Facebook likes and hearts.

The scheduling process is being automated. Tools such as Work-Fusion break high volume, complex data work into discrete tasks and algorithmically assign them to appropriate machine and human resources. These platforms look to improve human productivity by leveraging a combination of internal, outsourced, and crowdsourced workers. Customers control which types of workers contribute to crowdsourced work. Over time, humans are engaged only when algorithms face new obstacles or challenges for any particular task.

7. Continuous Feedback and Performance Review

The notion of the annual appraisal no longer resonates with a workforce that thrives on the 24/7 adrenaline rush of being liked, shared, and retweeted. Employees want frequent and instant feedback. At the same time, performance monitoring has extended into the physical and cognitive realms. Everything can and will be tracked, analyzed, and commented on.

Wearable devices such as health and fitness trackers are increasing in power and popularity. These wristbands and tags can be worn as fashion accessories, and monitor multiple aspects of health and fitness. It seems inevitable that some employees will be required to wear these devices as a condition of employment, while others may expect employers to provide them.

Additionally, brain-scanning technologies are already in place to monitor rising and falling emotion levels, concentration, and productivity. When used properly and ethically, with complete employee autonomy over whether they opt in or opt out, these technologies could present HR with new opportunities to monitor workforce health and wellbeing in a truly comprehensive manner. Data collected from wearables and brain monitors could be analyzed using AI to enable continual performance review and feedback.

A range of predictions and research surveys highlight the growing focus on physical and mental performance monitoring:

- Tractica predicts more than 75 million wearables will permeate the workplace by 2020.[19]
- Gartner estimates that by the end of 2018, two million employees will be required to wear health and fitness tracking devices as a condition of employment.[20]
- A PWC survey found 49% believe wearable technology will increase workplace efficiency, while 37% expect their company to adopt the latest technology even if it doesn't directly influence their work; 67% of respondents said that employers should pay for their device; only 25% of said they would not trust any company with personal information associated with wearable technology.[21]

8. Workplace Practices and Business Dress – Small Footprint Workplaces

As societal expectations and concerns shift, the workplace must adapt. As the modern workforce, Millennials, and younger workers (Gen Z) enter a societal age concerned with efficient use of talent, responsible practice, clean energy, conservation, ecological responsibility, and a greater focus on mindful business, the structure and ethos of organizations will inevitably change.

These concerns also drive questions about the external and internal design of buildings and the avoidance of ostentatious displays of corporate wealth and power. As workforces shrink through technological advances, firms must be even more mindful of their total physical, energetic, and environmental footprint. HR has a critical role here in acting as the guardian of corporate conscience and as a conduit between leaders and employees. Technology can play a critical role in supporting the dialogue.

9. Flexible Benefits – Salary, Health, Discounts, Location, Hours, Opportunity

As new discoveries on brain science and human behavior are emerging—and companies are using analytics to achieve improved results—HR will begin to arm itself with the tools and insights of a scientist to achieve better performances from their workforces. As neuroscience delivers ever-more valuable, high-level insights into the nuances of human behavior and performance, our notions and understanding of performance in the workplace will alter. Instead of managing a workforce with a one-size-fits-all approach, HR will be able to treat each employee as a "workforce of one" with unique needs and preferences, and customize employee incentives accordingly.

Technology is also enabling a buffet-style approach to selecting the benefits package that works for each employee. While one may prefer purely financial rewards to help save for a new home, another may opt for access to significant discounts on critical purchases such as holidays and cars.

For some, training and development might be prioritized while others opt for health insurance and gym membership. For example, Millennials and Gen Z are increasingly citing work-life balance, security, and stability as their priorities from employment, and employers must recognize the new expectations of them in the design of jobs, contracts, and benefits packages. An HR strategy based on a personalized approach needs to consider wellbeing and work-life balance as an essential component of a broader engagement model.

10. Total Wellbeing and the Enhanced Employee – Insuring the Cyborg Worker

Changing expectations of young workers and increased neuro-scientific knowledge are altering our perceptions of wellbeing in the workplace. We are witnessing the increasing use of performance-enhancing nootropic drugs and supplements to enhance cognitive performance in the workforce. Health and safety policies and company health insurance could be radically disrupted by the augmentation of human workers, the creation of cyborg workers, or the development of synthetic beings to carry out work deemed unpleasant or dangerous.

HR will need to review health and safety policies continually to meet the ever-changing physical nature of their employees. The blurring of the lines between human being, enhanced being, and fully augmented being will require HR to have a cutting-edge view of the nature of a person and an adaptive take on health policy.

The Most Critical Role of HR

As the world's obsession with digital transformation and AI increases, the focus inevitably shifts to the C-suite and the IT function, as together they must deliver the necessary technological infrastructure and business transformation. However, these change programs are doomed to undershoot their targets or fail completely if we don't take a step back and focus on the people dimension. Hence, HR has a critical role to play here in ensuring that change is managed properly and that our people genuinely are at the heart of the story. While technology can do more and more of our work, it will be a critical part of HR's role to ensure we are creating a very human future.

- *When developing next generation resourcing strategies, how will HR help determine the right balance between humans, augmented humans, external partners, and technology for a particular project, role, or task?*
- *How can HR ensure that it is perceived as a strategic partner and an equal voice in the process of organizational transformation?*
- *What impact would completely customized employee benefit packages have on how we measure and reward performance across the organization and promote ourselves externally?*

A version of this article was originally published in *HR Agenda* under the title "HR Technology: Faster Smarter More Human."

Driving Online Sales Growth – Winning in the Wild World

By Rohit Talwar and Steve Wells

How might businesses drive a step change in online sales performance in the coming years?

Many businesses no longer need convincing that online sales are becoming ever-more important. They see the potential to reach bigger audiences and generate massive uplifts in sales—if we get it right. Even those who have been selling online for some time are beginning to understand the true scale of the opportunity and acknowledge the potential to drive exponential sales growth.

But it all seems so complex: How can we succeed online when it appears to be changing by the day? What do we need to do tomorrow? How much should we be spending? What if we get it wrong? Everyone wants answers to the same questions. Here we explore practical tactics for those that sense the opportunity and are willing to invest some time and money in pursuit of the prize.

Some have pursued relatively modest goals and been pleasantly surprised at how much a good online presence can impact their revenues. The most spectacular winners to date in the online world have embraced the opportunity and developed a "digital mindset" which they continue to evolve in line with new thinking about how to use the internet as a sales channel. As a result, they are delivering exponential growth in online performance.

Others are being more ambitious still, and starting with the goal of developing businesses that can create a billion or more customers using the power of the mobile internet. So, whatever our ambition, how do we get started or take the next few steps? Below we have outlined four elements to focus on in your next steps plan.

1. Learning What Works

You can't delegate your own mindset change. You have to invest time reading and networking to learn about what others are doing online. Don't be afraid to ask basic questions—they can provide very powerful insights. Our top three areas to focus on when talking to others would be:

- *Results* – Establish that there's value to be gained. What proportion of revenues comes from online sales? How has that changed since they started selling online? How long did it take to generate meaningful online sales? How much comes from mobile? How does profitability compare to other sales approaches? What have they spent on creating and running their online offering? What are their online targets going forward?
- *Actions* – Understand how they got here. How did they start? What are they doing today? What tactics worked and which were abandoned? What external support did they use? How did/do they raise awareness and drive people to their site? What does their "conversion process" look like to take site visitors from interest to purchase? What would they do differently if starting again? What do the plan to do next? *Management* – How do they manage online sales? Who's in charge? What resources do they have involved? How do they deal with conflicts between the online and physical sales teams? How's that changed over time? What's next?

2. Think Mobile

People's interactions with the online world are increasingly happening via their mobiles and the trend is likely to continue. Whether they are using apps or accessing the internet, they will be doing it on their mobile devices and the functionality will get ever smarter. If you know where things are likely to be going, you can bear that in mind when developing your online offering. So, many now start by designing their website and app to work on mobile devices first and then adapt it for the bigger screen.

We can expect connectivity speeds to get faster, meaning we can share more video information about our products and services. Devices and apps are also likely to get more intelligent—smart software will increasingly block unwanted ads and calls and screen incoming callers on behalf of the user. What are the critical messages that you want to convey to get you past these electronic guardians?

3. From Research to Action

The key to success is willingness to experiment and try what's worked for others. This means putting people on the web team that like learning, testing, and refining ideas and who don't mind dumping stuff that isn't delivering. If step change is your goal, then make sure you've researched companies who've done that. Then create a plan of actions that you want to try—from promotions and banner exchanges, to social media campaigns, and low-cost sponsorships. Have a 3 to 6 month schedule of what you want to try each week or month, monitor it, measure it, learn from it, and refine the strategy. Be willing to adapt plans in the face of evidence from the actions you are taking.

Keep looking out for new ideas and encourage the whole business to do the same and generate their own ideas. The key here is being honest about what you are worried about in relation to your online presence, e.g. damaging your reputation, irritating customers who see a lower price than the one they paid, or giving too much away to your competition. The more you share of these concerns, the more your team can think about how to address them when seeking out and generating ideas.

4. Finding Customers – Look for What's Hiding in Plain Sight

Look for opportunities to present yourself where potential customers are already. Airports, train stations, shopping centers, sporting events, festivals, markets, and other live events all have ready-made audiences. Taking pop-up stalls in these venues gives you an opportunity to try out a different way of meeting and engaging with potential customers and then encouraging them to provide you with their details so you can continue the relationship. I may love the locally made chocolates that I tasted from a pop-up stall in Cambridge station; connecting online means I can keep buying the goodies even if I never see the stall again.

There are now countless examples of players who have gone from nothing to exponential growth by capturing customer interest in the online world. There are also many who've evolved from a physical presence to a purely online operation because of the efficiencies it can bring. Others have failed spectacularly to crack the online opportunity.

The keys to success lie in learning continuously, asking the right questions, recognizing how the technology is evolving, planning carefully, experimenting constantly, and involving the right people. Success also requires us to be clear on our goals and concerns, and then adopting an iterative, experimental, and constantly evolving approach to what we actually do online and to how we go about attracting potential customers.

- *What are the key priorities for the next evolution of your online presence?*
- *What tactics are you adopting in both the physical and online environment to drive people to your site?*
- *How are you involving staff in the process of generating ideas for the evolution of your site?*

A version of this article was originally published in *Sales Initiative* under the title "Driving exponential online growth by reaching new digital customers."

Building Treasury's Digital Culture – Harnessing Next Generation Technologies

By Rohit Talwar

How might technology innovation impact the future of the treasury function?

Corporate treasury is a classic example of core business functions that will be reinvented in the coming years. Perhaps the biggest challenges are those of raising the function's technological literacy and evolving genuinely digital mindsets. As the digital disruption typhoon sweeps across the business landscape, surviving the storm requires senior treasurers to raise the understanding of themselves and their teams of what emerging technologies enable in terms of functionality and new ways of thinking and doing business.

Opportunities are arising through new FinTech solutions for treasury functions to bypass banks and other providers—but understanding and realizing the opportunities requires deep digital literacy. Technology advances enable radically different concepts underpinned by dramatically different ways of looking at treasury activity, hence digital culture needs to encompass both the emerging technology and the associated mindsets.

At its heart, a digital mindset means seeing everything as data rather than physical objects represented by data—and hence something that can be analyzed and manipulated in ever-more clever and complex ways. For example, automotive industry leaders are starting to see that the biggest value in cars lies in software and the data it generates about every aspect of the car and what the passengers do while travelling.

The car has become a monetizable data generation platform and now offers the potential for constantly updateable revenue streams rather than a single fixed purchase. With the rise of Tesla's autonomous vehicles and similar digitally minded manufacturers such as Local Motors, who crowdsources their 3D printed car designs, a car is no longer just a means of transportation—it becomes a physical embodiment of digital products and services.

Successful digitally literate business leaders in treasury will need to embrace disruptive technologies such as artificial intelligence (AI), blockchain, cloud computing, hyperconnectivity, and process automation. These technologies enable the creation of tools that can help increase efficiency and effectiveness, and create more value for internal customers and others who treasury connects with.

As financial services firms and central banks start adopting blockchain and digital/crypto currencies, the pace of change in the marketplace will only accelerate. China is exploring the technology with the intent of transforming its entire finance sector while others are looking at blockchain as a platform for frictionless sale and distribution of equities, currencies, bonds, and other assets.

The secure and irrevocable nature of blockchain transactions coupled with the reduction in transaction fees makes it an attractive proposition for executing direct peer-to-peer transactions between counterparties without the need for intermediaries such as banks. Artificial intelligence also offers the potential for smarter analysis and automation of many routine tasks.

Positive digital treasury cultures will explore ways of enhancing the role of people in the organization through AI rather than simply automating the work. Finding deeper, meaningful ways to connect to employees and encourage their best work, and providing worthwhile experiences for both employees and internal customers—i.e. building relationships—will be the true hallmarks of the digitally enlightened organization.

- *What does treasury leadership need to unlearn in order to enable the emergence of a digital culture?*
- *What opportunities are there on offer from banks and other vendors to conduct safe, low cost trials of next-generation treasury technology?*
- *What modeling is your organization doing of the financial impact of moving to blockchain and cryptocurrencies for key processes in treasury and finance?*

A version originally published in *Treasury Today* under the title "Building Treasury's Digital Culture."

Conclusion – Critical Shifts Driving the Reinvention

By Rohit Talwar

What fundamental shifts might characterize the emerging future?

Drivers of the Revolution and Riders of the Storm

Through the pages of this book, two things have hopefully become abundantly clear. Firstly, the old order of everything either has been challenged, is in the process of upheaval, or will be disrupted in the next few years. Secondly, our notions of a linear, controllable, and defensible progression to the future are being overturned. The future is being reinvented, and we are simultaneously playing the parallel roles of initiators, catalysts, investors, beneficiaries, and victims of the changes that will play out.

We are at such an early stage in the change process that it is impossible to know the likely outcomes of all this change. Nor can we pinpoint with absolute accuracy the key themes and shifts that will have the biggest influence in the reimagining of life, society, and business. However, it is clear that there are strong candidates that are likely to have more of a bearing than others. Whilst these are not all unfolding at the same pace, the instantaneous nature of the Internet and a 24/7 news cycle can make it seem that way. Here we identify twenty-one key shifts we see taking place that will be major drivers, or significant enablers, of the future reinvented.

Life and Society

1. *Harassment and Assault: From why me to #metoo* – The #metoo change movement will gather momentum, and victims of sexual abuse and harassment around the world will continue to find the courage and support to challenge the offenders.The abuser's fall from grace will be massive and visible—encompassing the church, the military, the professions, sports, media, entertainment, politics, and business. Successive waves of public apologies, enforced resignations, and early retirements will lead to fundamental changes of policy, practice, and protection in all these sectors and drive a shift in the balance of power towards the victims.

2. *Spirituality: From possession to purpose* – As society becomes more technologically dependent and pressurized, people are increasingly looking for a sense of purpose that goes beyond material achievements and possessions into the realms of spiritual fulfilment. From religion to meditation and yoga, we are pursuing alternative routes to enlightenment. There is also a growing sense that the source—of the power and guiding inspiration we seek—may lie within us rather than outside.

3. *Privacy: From birthright to asset* – In many nations, the right to privacy has, in the past, been seen as a birthright. Government policy and technology have changed that. Governments have gradually assumed the right to know more about us, and the major online players and personal technology providers have amassed vast stores of information on our lives.

   Most of us have scant knowledge of what's being collected or how it's being used. We have effectively traded our privacy for the right to access certain services and information. Ironically, smart personal technology may gradually give us back control over that information and curtail the extent of the surveillance capitalism we are subjected to. We may increasingly be able to decide the tradeoffs we make with our personal information and when we'll chose to trade that asset in return for things that we value.

4. *Mental Health: From my little secret to our collective responsibility* – There are rising levels of pre-clinical and clinical mental health issues across society in both developed and developing nations. Stress levels are also expected to rise as the pace of technological unemployment increases. Organizations will be judged on their capacity to address and minimize workplace stress.

5. *Relationships: From monogamous to multivariant* – The conventional model of a monogamous relationship with a lifetime partner is being challenged in multiple ways. The most obvious example is that of people pursuing polyamory and open relationships in a transparent manner. Alongside these models, we see multi-functional relationship models where one person might fulfill their romantic, child raising, emotional, and intellectual needs through separate partners of possibly different genders.

6. *Parenting and Home Making: From bed maker to bread winner* – Women are consistently outperforming men at every level of the education system globally. Gradually, barriers to opportunity and glass ceilings are being dismantled and pay gaps eroded. The pace is expected to quicken—changing workplace cultures and driving a reversal of parenting and home maker roles within the family.

7. *Sex: From constrained to conscious* – As people seek more meaning and purpose from life overall, a major shift in attitudes is taking place around sex. Clearly, many are still focused on consumption, influenced by pornography, and adopting a balance sheet accounting approach - demanding reciprocity for every act. There is though, a growing interest in a more conscious approach that sees sex as part of the process of deepening connection. The coming together of spirituality and the pursuit of a more enlightened approach to sex are part of what lies behind the increasing popularity of connection based practices such as tantra and orgasmic meditation.

8. *Augmentation: From human to post-human* – A range of chemical, genetic, electronic, and bio-mechanical augmentations

are starting to allow us to change the very nature of being human. To keep up with technology and the pace of modern life, we will be opting for enhancements, from extending life expectancy and changing our genomic make-up, to enhancing physical strength and augmenting our cognitive powers.

9. *Education Systems: From control to nurture* – Education systems around the world are widely seen to be glaringly out of date and unfit for purpose. Technology is expected to play an increasing role, with some reports suggesting that it could take over 75% of what teachers do. The opportunity here is to reinvest that time in nurturing focused tasks rather than student control. Teaching roles will gradually shift to helping pupils learn skills—such as collaboration, problem solving, scenario thinking, and accelerated learning techniques—that will be applicable whatever their future might hold. The Internet is also driving interest in home schooling as the best content becomes available for free.

10. *Work: From defining purpose to pastime of choice* – Across the planet, people are beginning to understand that technologies such as artificial intelligence (AI) and robotics could mean that we may need a lot less people to work in paid jobs in the future. Concepts such as universal basic incomes and services may become a reality in this next decade to help people fund a reasonable lifestyle.

    Those that do choose to work may do so simply for social connection and the physical or intellectual challenge, rather than as a means to earn money. Phrases like "long-term unemployed" and "burden on society" may start to disappear from society's vocabulary as the realization grows that we might just be seeing the beginnings of the end of work.

Politics and Economics

11. *Politics: From the center to the edges* – We can expect to see a continued shift towards, and growing calls for, devolution of power to a more local level. From Brexit to separatist movements in Catalonia and beyond, pressure will rise to escape the distant hand

of central control. Not all will succeed in securing independence, or in making a success of it, but the pressure will mount.

12. *The US Presidency: From sovereign standards to situational solutions* – President Trump has challenged all traditional notions of how he should conduct his role and what constitutes acceptable Presidential behavior. From his use of Twitter and deliberate misrepresentation of facts through to his direct attacks on individuals—Mr. Trump has effectively widened the Presidential playing field.

13. *Transparency: From nothing to say to nowhere to hide* – Governments, institutions, and individuals will find it increasingly difficult to keep anything secret. For at least the next decade, hacker collectives, and those who support them, will have the resources to access critical data and make it public. Whistle blowers and investigative journalists will keep the spotlight on abuses of power, and the Internet will provide channels to put the content in front of the public.

14. *Money: From controlled to chaotic* – The rise of digital currencies such as Bitcoin have challenged the notion that only central banks could issue globally tradeable forms of money. The decade ahead is likely to see a proliferation of cryptocurrencies, and governments and financial exchanges authorizing their use in trading. At the same time, governmental desire to know what people are doing with their money will clash head on with the anonymity that goes with a Bitcoin transaction. The outcome will be a growing level of complexity and confusion over the potential to transition to a single global currency.

15. *Financial Control: From institutions to networks* – There is continual erosion of the financial sectors' monopoly on the processing of transactions and the management of our funds. New FinTech ventures are allowing us to bypass the traditional players to transfer funds between us and raise money from each other directly. The advent of Bitcoin as a currency and blockchain as a mutually assured distributed transaction

ledger allow for counter-parties to settle directly with each other without ever going through the traditional middlemen.

16. *Tax: From gaming the system to a fairer game* – Governments around the world will increasingly seek to grow their tax revenues, close loopholes, and simplify the systems. They will also look to make those systems smarter and more powerful through the use of AI. They also want to be seen to be creating a fairer and more balanced system. At the same time, the risks of technological unemployment could reduce income taxes and sales taxes and increase the pressure to collect more from larger firms and higher earners.

17. *Brexit: From bravado to fluidity* – The hardened negotiating stance being taken early on by both the United Kingdom (UK) and the European Union (EU) will continue to soften and reshape. Tough talk will be replaced by the pragmatism of finding a solution that doesn't create total havoc for the UK, but which still discourages other EU members from trying to leave. The challenge for the UK will be to leave the EU in name, whilst establishing policies and mechanisms that allow individuals and businesses to behave as though they are still members.

Business

18. *Intelligence: From human to artificial* – The pace of development in AI is likely to continue at breathtaking speed. Inevitably there will be a growing tendency to replace humans with their more consistent, reliable, and faster machine counterparts.

19. *Business Mindset: From linear to exponential* – The exponential growth in performance of many technologies is driving firms to pursue similar improvement rates across their business in sectors as diverse as construction and car manufacturing.

20. *Knowledge: From expert curated to discovery led* – Technology is eroding the expertise base of traditional advice giver roles from lawyers and consultants, to accountants and clinicians. Increasingly, AI tools will help us seek, sort, and

analyze far greater volumes of data than any human can, whilst ensuring that we are drawing on the most up-to-date information. Rather than paying experts to provide a lot of information and opinion to justify their fees, the new tools will increasingly enable us to find the point information and decision options most relevant to our current situation.

21. *Employment: From castles to cottages* – Whilst the number of organizations with a turnover of US$100 million may grow, the number of people collectively employed by larger national and global businesses is likely to fall as a percentage of the total workforce. Hence, a multi-fold increase is required in the number of small to medium businesses to fill the short- to medium-term employment gap. Clearly, as discussed above, the longer term picture is harder to determine. To support the growth of small and micro start-ups, the amount of support provided to entrepreneurs will need to increase at least exponentially if they are to take up the slack.

- *Which of these shifts to do you expect to have the greatest bearing on your life and your work?*
- *Which shifts could bring about the greatest benefit to humanity?*
- *Which shifts will have the most transformational impacts on society?*

References

[1]World Economic Forum. 01/19/2016. https://www.weforum.org/agenda/2016/01/
what–is–the–fourth–industrial–revolution/

[2]Organization for Economic Co-operation and Development. 2000. https://www.oecd.
org/site/schoolingfortomorrowknowledgebase/themes/ict/41284692.pdf

[3]Colorado Department of Education http://www.coloradotechliteracy.org/org/
documentation/module1/definition.htm

[4]International Society for Technology in Education. 6/25/2014. https://www.iste.org/
explore/ArticleDetail?articleid=101

[5]All Coins News. 3/15/2016. http://allcoinsnews.com/2016/03/15/
major-us-law-firm-highlights-blockchain-revolution-in-financial-services/

[6 13 14]Australian Financial Review. 5/30/2016. http://www.afr.com/technology/
blockchain-smart-contracts-to-disrupt-lawyers-20160529-gp6f5e

[7]Tech Republic. 8/2/2016. http://www.techrepublic.com/article/
bitcoin-blockchain-attorneys-at-law-one-firms-big-switch/

[8 9]Bloomberg. 8/17/2016. https://bol.bna.com/
will-blockchain-affect-your-practice-or-firm-perspective/

[10]Coindesk. 10/22/2015. http://www.coindesk.com/
london-law-firm-to-digitise-contracts-using-bitcoin-technology/

[11]Australian Financial Review. 6/19/2016. http://www.afr.com/technology/
lawyers-prepare-for-driverless-ma-as-smart-contract-era-dawns-20160616-gpknyz

[12]The Guardian. 8/2/2016. https://www.theguarian.com/small-business-network/2016/aug/02/blockchain-businesses-embark-on-world-changing-projects

[15]Slock.it. 4/26/2016. https://blog.slock.it/announcing-dao-link-the-bridge-between-blockchain-and-brick-and-mortar-companies-9510ba04d236#.4kdirkn1a

[16]Inside Bitcoins. 6/10/2017. http://insidebitcoins.com/news/russia-and-china-may-digitize-their-currencies-with-ethereum/55881

[17]World Economic Forum. 2016. http://reports.weforum.org/future-of-jobs-2016/chapter-1-the-future-of-jobs-and-skills/

[18]The New York Times. 2/25/2016. https://www.nytimes.com/2016/02/28/magazine/what-google-learned-from-its-quest-to-build-the-perfect-team.html

[19]Tractica. 4/8/2015. https://www.tractica.com/newsroom/press-releases/more-than-75-million-wearable-devices-to-be-deployed-in-enterprise-and-industrial-environments-by-2020/

[20]Gartner. 10/6/2015. https://www.gartner.com/newsroom/id/3143718

[21]PWC. 2016. https://www.pwc.com/ee/et/publications/pub/pwc-cis-wearables.pdf

Fast Future

Fast Future is a professional foresight firm specializing in delivering keynote speeches, executive education, research, and consulting on the emerging future and the impacts of change for global clients. In 2015 we created a new model of publishing led by three futurists—Rohit Talwar, Steve Wells, and April Koury. As a publisher, our goal is to profile the latest thinking of established and emerging futurists, foresight researchers, and future thinkers from around the world, and to make those ideas accessible to the widest possible audience in the shortest possible time.

Our *FutureScapes* book series is designed to address a range of critical agenda setting futures topics with in-depth contributions from global thought leaders and cutting-edge future thinkers. We cover topics that we believe are relevant to individuals, governments, businesses, and civil society. Our *Fast Future* series is designed to provide rapid insights into the emerging future with a collection of short, hard hitting articles. These explore different trends, developments, forces, and ideas shaping the future and how we can respond in a manner that best serves humanity.

Our first book, *The Future of Business*, provides 60 fast moving chapters and 566 pages of cutting-edge thinking from 62 future thinkers in 21 different countries on four continents. Traditional publishers would take two years to deliver a book of this magnitude; we completed the journey from idea to publication in just 19 weeks.

We have also created an innovative business model that bypasses most of the traditional publishing practices and inefficiencies, embracing digital era exponential thinking and applying it to transform the publishing process, the distribution approach, and the profit sharing model. Our publishing model ensures that our authors, core team members, and partners on each book share in its success. Additionally, a proportion of profits are allocated to a development fund to finance causes related to the core topic.

We hope that our story and our approach to publishing are an inspiring example of how business is evolving and being reinvented in the digital era.

Over the coming years, Fast Future aims to publish the work of insightful and inspiring futurists and future thinkers. We are keen to receive proposals from potential authors and those interested in compiling and editing multi-contributor book as part of either the *FutureScapes* or *Fast Future* series.

For corporate or bulk orders of *The Future Reinvented, Beyond Genuine Stupidity, The Future of Business*, and *Technology vs. Humanity*, please contact karolina@fastfuture.com.

To book a keynote speaker, discuss an executive education, consulting, or research requirement, or explore partnership opportunities please contact rohit@fastfuture.com.

To submit a chapter idea or a book proposal, discuss ideas for curating and editing a multi-contributor project, or to enquire about permanent and internship opportunities, please contact info@fastfuture.com.

You can learn more about us at www.fastfuture.com.

We look forward to hearing from you!

Also Available from Fast Future

The Future of Business – Critical insights to a rapidly changing world from 62 future thinkers

The Future of Business explores how the commercial world is being transformed by the complex interplay between social, economic and political shifts, disruptive ideas, bold strategies and breakthroughs in science and technology. Over 60 contributors from 21 countries explore how the business landscape will be reshaped by factors as diverse as the modification of the human brain and body, 3D printing, alternative energy sources, the reinvention of government, new business models, artificial intelligence, blockchain technology, and the potential emergence of the *Star Trek* economy.

The *Fast Future* Book Series

This series of books is designed to provide clear and rapid insights into the trends, forces, developments, and ideas shaping the future and the possible scenarios that could arise. Each book contains a collection of short, hard hitting articles that explore different aspects of the emerging future and how we can respond in a manner that best serves humanity.

Fast Future 1: Beyond Genuine Stupidity – Ensuring AI Serves Humanity

The first book in the *Fast Future* series explores critical emerging issues arising from the rapid pace of development in artificial intelligence. The authors argue for a forward looking approach to the development and deployment of AI to ensure that it genuinely serves humanity's best interest. They present a compelling case to get beyond the genuine stupidity of narrow, short term, and alarmist thinking and look at AI from a long-term holistic perspective.

Available in 2018 from Fast Future

Unleashing Human Potential – The Future of AI in Business

The pace of business investment in and adoption of artificial intelligence is accelerating, and the level of interest and activity is rising across all sectors. The intention is to provide a diverse set of perspectives on where the technology is going, how it is being deployed in business today, and how the capabilities, applications, and impact of AI could evolve over the next 3 to 10 years.

50:50 – Scenarios for the Next 50 Years

Every year, on March 1st, citizens across the planet celebrate World Future Day and explore the possibilities of changes on the horizon. Fast Future is taking this opportunity of World Future Day 2018 to explore scenarios for the next 50 years by publishing 50 perspectives on possible futures from 50 different future thinkers around the world.

A Very Human Future – Pathways to Sustainable Abundance

A Very Human Future will explore how we can put humanity at the center of the story and harness advances in science and technology in service of the greater social good.

Visit www.fastfuture.com for more information.

Under Consideration

The landscape for potential publication topics is evolving rapidly and we are excited at the prospects of working on multi-author books under the *FutureScapes* and *Fast Future* series banners or partnering with innovative organizations who share our passion for exploring the future. We are currently considering books on a range of future related themes.

We are always interested to hear from authors who want to bring their ideas, knowledge, and insights to market with Fast Future.

Visit www.fastfuture.com for more information.